Short Takes

15 Contemporary Stories

Edited by Monica Wood

J. Weston Walch, Publisher
Portland, Maine

1 2 3 4 5 6 7 8 9 10

ISBN 0-8251-2102-7

J. Weston Walch, Publisher
P.O. Box 658 • Portland, Maine 04104-0658

Printed in the United States of America

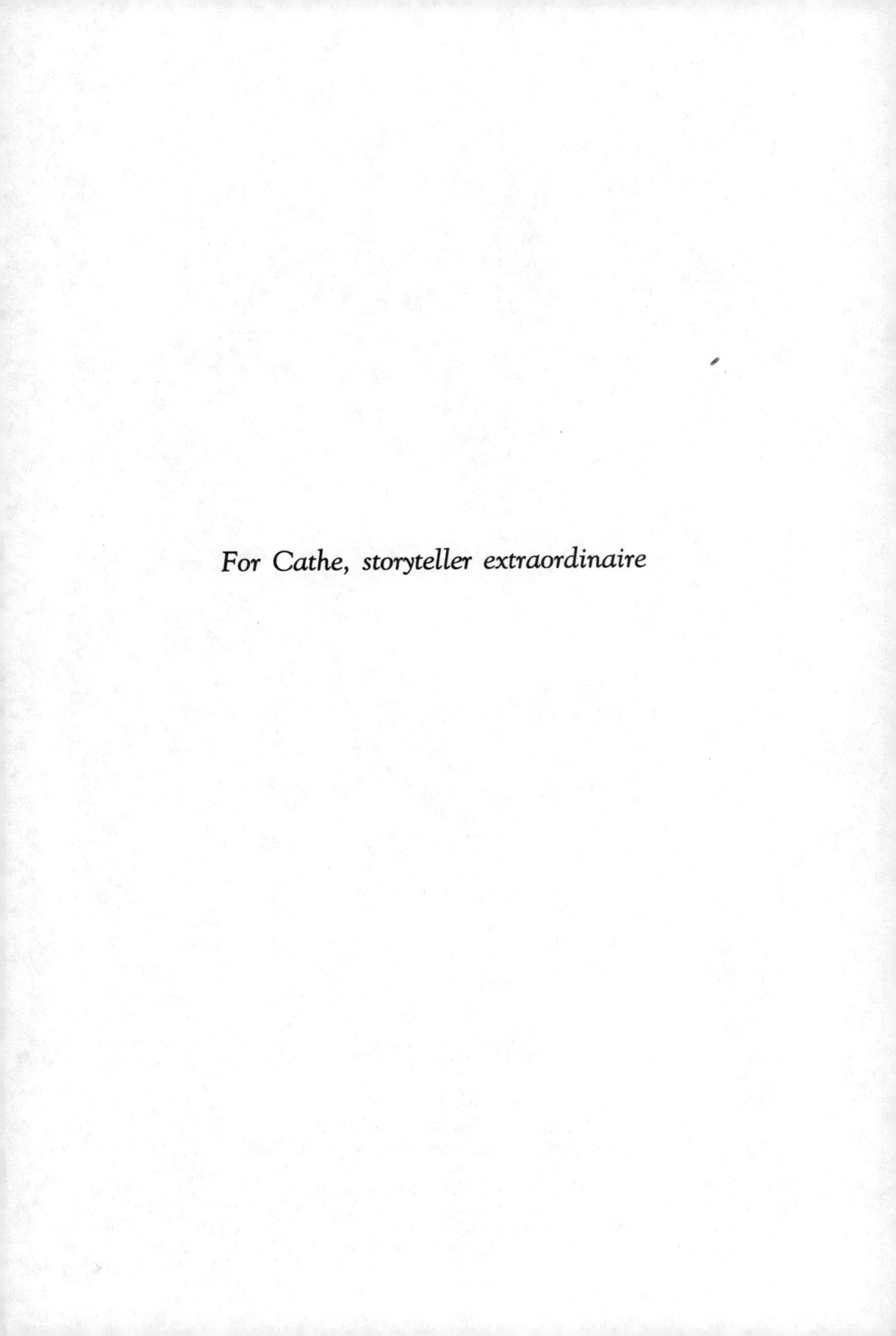

For Cathe, storyteller extraordinaire

Contents

Acknowledgments

"Bluestown" by Geoffrey Becker, first published in the *Chicago Tribune* and reprinted in *The North American Review*. Copyright © 1989 by Geoffrey Becker. Reprinted by permission of the author.

"Tickits" by Paul Milenski, as first published in *Quarterly West*, Spring/Summer 1984, reprinted in *Northwest*, *The Sunday Oregonian*, *Sunday*, *The Chicago Tribune Magazine*, *Facet*, *SUDDEN FICTION: AMERICAN SHORT-SHORT STORIES*, and *Inside Stories 4*, and as broadcast on National Public Radio's "The Sound of Writing" and as filmed in "Tickits," the University of Central Florida, School of Communication, Film Division. Reprinted by permission of the author.

"Feeding the Piranha" by Pamela Painter, first published in *The Atlantic Monthly*. Copyright © 1989; reprinted by permission of the author and Roberta Pryor, Inc.

"What Means Switch" by Gish Jen. Copyright © 1990 by Gish Jen. All rights reserved. Reprinted by permission of the author. "What Means Switch" originally appeared in *The Atlantic Monthly* in a slightly different form.

"Coyote v. Acme" by Ian Frazier. Reprinted by permission; copyright © Ian Frazier. Originally in *The New Yorker*.

"Two Fathers" by Charis W. Conn, first published in *The North American Review*. Copyright © 1987 by Charis W. Conn. Reprinted by permission of the author.

To the Student

Short Takes is a story anthology that, on the surface, probably resembles others you have seen. It contains a variety of stories, each one preceded by a short introduction and followed by some discussion questions. But look again. These stories have been plucked from recent issues of magazines you can find every month at the newsstands or in your library. These are the stories of living, breathing writers who live in the same world as you. This world—by turns absurd, poignant, heartbreaking, hopeful—is reflected in these stories.

When we think of literature we tend to look back: Dickens, Hawthorne, and Steinbeck are just three of the authors you have most likely become acquainted with through your high school English classes. But literature did not stop with these great writers. Every age, every decade, every day brings new writers with just as much potential for greatness. They take pen (or word processor) in hand to continue the tradition of delving into the contradictions and intricacies of the human heart. Here to make your acquaintance are fifteen of them.

Life is full of ulterior motives, and there is one behind this book. It is hoped that by reading these writers you will seek out more of their stories, in their collections or in other magazines; that you will discover other writers by reading the magazines in which these stories first appeared; and that you will understand why the word *literature* does not apply only to dead writers and old books.

So here they are: fifteen writers from your own time. Some of them will make you laugh. Some of them will make you cry. All of them will make you think. And if you have the energy and inclination, perhaps one day you will number yourself among them.

Bluestown

by Geoffrey Becker

(First appeared in the Chicago Tribune*)*

This vibrant story is about a young man who discovers the difference between truth and hope. Notice how the narrator uses his powers of observation—the ungenerous vibrations of a strange bar, the decor of a diner, or the simplicity of a New England town—to unwittingly prepare himself for the reality that comes at the end of the story.

About the Author

GEOFFREY BECKER grew up in Princeton, New Jersey. After graduating from Colby College in Maine in 1980, he spent a few months traveling in Europe as a street musician. He currently lives with his dog in Iowa City, Iowa, where he works for the University of Iowa and hosts a local blues jam on Monday nights. "Bluestown" won the *Chicago Tribune's* Nelson Algren Award and was mentioned as one of the distinguished stories of the year in *THE BEST AMERICAN SHORT STORIES 1990*. Geoff's stories have appeared in a number of magazines.

hen I was fifteen, my father showed up at our high school and stood outside the door of Mr. Margin's history class wearing his leather jacket, waving a pink piece of paper. It was a September afternoon, sunny but not too hot, the sky bright blue. I had been alternately staring out the window and making eyes at Lucy Westbrook, who sat opposite me and had probably the nicest body in the whole school. Mr. Margin stopped lecturing (the subject was, I think, slavery) and went to the door, then gestured for me to step out into the hall with him.

"You're excused, Spencer," he said. "It seems you've forgotten something."

I didn't know what he was talking about, but the prospect of getting out of that stuffy classroom was an unexpected gift.

"Your doctor's appointment, Spence." said my dad. He looked at his watch. "We're late already." He had this concerned, fatherly expression on his face. He looked at Mr. Margin in commiseration. "I knew he'd forget. He's known about this for weeks."

"It's my experience," said Mr. Margin, "that given half a chance, these kids will forget anything. Get a move on, Spencer—read the next chapter for tomorrow's class." He gave me an affectionate smack on the shoulder.

"Kids," said my dad to him, then led me down the hall. When we got to the front entrance, he looked both ways, then began to run. He took off across the front lawn, past a group of kids sharing a joint, nearly tripping over a girl who was stretched out in the sun. I ran after him, thinking that this time he had finally, truly lost it. When I caught up with him at his car, a '67 Buick station wagon with a wired-on front bumper, I could see the back of it was loaded with equipment—all his guitars, an amplifier, and a suitcase. I got in the passenger side as he started up the engine.

"What's going on?" I asked when I'd caught my breath.

He slipped on a pair of aviator sunglasses. "It's way too nice a day to hang out in school," he said. "I figured you ought to get sprung."

He loved to break rules—it was one of the things I liked best about him. It was also part of the reason he'd been banished, several years before, from the small ranch house where my mother and I still lived along with Hal, her new husband. My dad, a few gray hairs just beginning to appear on his shaggy head, now inhabited a small apartment downtown, over Angelo's Pizza and Calzone. I still saw a lot of him, probably more than my mother would have liked. He was only supposed to get me one day a week, but I usually went over to his place after school and hung around listening to albums, or playing cards. Since his work, when he had any, was at night, he was home afternoons. He liked to talk about the old days, when rock and roll was still counter-culture and not just something else to show on TV. We'd sit up there in his cluttered apartment, albums and cassette tapes strewn over the floor, the smell of pizza wafting up through the floorboards, and he'd tell me how he was never really cut out to be a family man. Possessions and responsibilities made him nervous, even things like his stereo and television. But even so, whenever he got some money, he'd spend it on a new toy—a phase-shifter or a compressor, or maybe a graphic EQ, and together we'd spend hours fooling with the knobs and buttons.

He played me albums too, everything from Robert Johnson and Lightnin' Hopkins to Jimi Hendrix and Duane Allman. Guitar, he said, was the only instrument on which you could really play the blues, and at fifteen I was a blues expert. I was familiar with all sorts of obscure, Chicago-based players, most of whom seemed to be named Milton or Melvin. I even thought I knew what it meant to have the blues. In school I covered my notebooks with drawings of guitars and amps. My prize possession was a Muddy Waters t-shirt he brought me back from New York once, and which I wore so often my mother had to swipe it from my room just to get it washed. With my friends I smoked cigarettes and kept my hands plunged deep into my pockets, nodding in time to an imaginary beat. What I liked above all things was the tortured sound of a guitar string bent almost to the point of breaking.

I asked about all the equipment, and he explained that he had an audition in Montreal for a gig with a new band that had backing, a recording contract—everything but the right guitarist. He went to a lot of auditions, but this seemed major—there was an intensity on his face that I couldn't remember seeing. When I asked him how they happened to come up with *his* name for the audition, he just smiled and said "a friend of a friend." I believed him. My dad had a lot of friends.

He made a living as a guitarist, sort of. It always seemed like he was on the verge of success when something would happen. My mother said he brought it on himself, but as far as I could see, he just ran into a lot of bad luck. For a while he'd pinned his hopes on Madeleine—an emaciated redhead with an enormous, whiskey-steeped voice. He worked with her for about a year, then she got born again and moved to Wisconsin. Another time he left his car unlocked and all his instruments were stolen, so for months he had to borrow equipment. But he stayed optimistic, full of plans, and even my mom, on the uncomfortable occasion when she would run into him at the supermarket or the drugstore, found it hard to be angry with him. She didn't like us spending time together and said he was a bad role model, but he could always do something dumb, like wiggle his eyebrows at her, or juggle a couple of avocados, to smooth things out.

We went to the Dairy Queen and had black and white milkshakes. That was where the greasers hung out, and the parking lot was full of them: slicked-back hair, big combs sticking out of the back pockets of their polyester pants. They leaned against jacked-up cars, smoked cigarettes, ignored the girlfriends who lounged next to them, all hairspray and lip gloss, car radios blaring. With his leather jacket, worn-out jeans and shades, my dad was easily the coolest-looking person there. I liked the way we could just hang out together on the hood of the Buick, feeling the hot metal under our legs, sipping a cold shake.

"Jimi," he said. It was something we'd done since I was little—calling each other by the names of dead guitarists. I got to be Jimi, and he was Duane, after Duane Allman, who was definitely the closest thing to a hero in his life. Nobody'd ever played slide like Duane, or ever would.

"They sent me bucks to cover expenses."

"Great," I said. "That means they're serious."

He shrugged. "I guess. The way I see it, if I drive up, it costs me next to nothing and I pocket the difference. What do you say? Feel like a road trip?"

I could think of nothing I felt like more. An image of the two of us cruising north through New England flashed through my mind like the trailer for a sixties road movie. But my mother was going to be a problem.

He lowered his voice. "We won't tell her—we'll just leave a note saying you're with me, and when we get back, I'll take all the heat."

A note from him wasn't going to get me out of anything, but I wanted to go, so I convinced myself it was a workable plan. After all, it would just be a couple of days.

"It feels a little like running away from home," I said,

enjoying the idea. A friend of mine, Nicky Dormer, had run away from home for four days the year before, and afterwards he'd seemed to me years older.

"Jimi, my man," he answered, massaging my shoulders. "It is impossible to run away from home with your own father."

My mom was still at work. He drove by the house and I ran upstairs to get a toothbrush while he stood in the kitchen penciling a quick note in his own, peculiarly recognizable handwriting—an angular sort of chicken scratch. When I came back down he was still laboring over it. It was odd seeing him there, back in the house for the first time in years. He looked uncomfortable, out of place. I looked at what he wrote, but it wasn't until we were in the car and heading out of town that I asked him about it.

"Hey, Duane," I said, "how come you put down that we were going to Virginia?"

"Just a precaution," he said. "In case she decides to call the cops, it'll buy us some time."

As soon as we were on the road, he slipped in a cassette of the Allman Brothers doing "Statesboro Blues," and I kicked my feet up on the dashboard. The music almost seemed to be powering the car. I'd seen pictures from back when I was only about three or four, when my dad practically *was* Duane Allman. He wore his hair all the way down his back and had the same mutton-chop sideburns. The day after Duane died on his motorcycle, my dad managed to get into an accident on his. He broke a leg and an arm, but he also got an out of court settlement that was enough to buy our house, as well as a good PA system and a couple of guitars. He was set up—twenty-five years old, a high school graduate with a wife, a kid and his own place. Things started to happen. Weird people would come over in the middle of the night to hang out, and in the morning there'd be spilled beer and cigarette burns in the carpet. My mom and he would fight, then he'd disappear for a couple of days at a time. Afterwards he'd always try to make up for it by doing something real normal, like mowing the lawn, or taking the three of us out to the movies.

Finally, she just told him to move. I was nine. "Jimi," he said to me, "I'm not going anywhere." He wrote his new phone number on the inside of a book of matches and put it in my hand.

We stopped for gas at a turnpike service station and he pulled out his wallet. It was stuffed with bills, more money than I'd ever seen him with at one time. He removed a ten and gave it to me. "Candy bars," he said, solemnly.

I got change and pushed quarters into the machine until I had extracted four Snickers, our favorite. Then, on impulse, I also bought a pair of cheap amber-tinted sunglasses that were aviators like his. They were small on me and rode high on the bridge of my nose. They cost six dollars and were probably worth about forty-nine cents, but I bought them anyway. When I got back to the car he lifted them off and bent the flimsy frame across the middle, just slightly, then put them back on me.

"That's it," he said. "Now you're cooking."

As we drove, we talked about Canada. Neither of us had ever been, so we made a list of things it was famous for.

"Canadian bacon," I offered.

"Salmon," he said.

"The Expos."

"Draft dodgers."

"Niagara Falls."

"That's in America," he said.

"Only part of it. The other part is Canadian."

He looked over at me. "Who figured that out?"

"It makes sense. It's a natural divider. That's how they

always divide up countries, states too." When he didn't say anything, I fell silent for a little while, thinking about how things divided. How did they know exactly where Canada stopped and America began? It was all just water—there couldn't be any clear line like on a map. I thought about me and my dad—I was halfway to thirty, and he was halfway to seventy. I always had an idea that when I turned eighteen I would experience some obvious transformation into adulthood, but now that I was getting closer, I wondered. From far away things always seemed so simple and clear-cut, but up close they blurred. The twenty years that separated me from my dad suddenly seemed like nothing at all, not in the huge scheme of things. I liked that.

We crossed the Vermont border around sunset and stopped for burgers at a place with two enormous trucks parked outside. It was a classic roadside diner, but somehow not quite real—everything in it was brand-new, though styled to look like the mid-fifties. It was someone's idea of what a diner should have looked like—lots of chrome and mirrors and a big, colorful jukebox. I put a quarter in and selected two songs.

"So if they like you, does that mean you'll have to move to Canada?" I asked.

"Could be," he said, nodding. "I don't know. It all depends."

I pictured his apartment over the pizzeria and tried to imagine someone else living there, but it just didn't seem like a real possibility. "I'd miss you," I said. "Where would I hang out?"

He tapped the tabletop with his fork. "Well, let's not count our chickens. They may not want me at all. I'm getting kind of old for this line of work."

"How can you say that? Look at the Stones. Look at . . . " I tried to think of someone else. "B.B. King. He's still going, and he must be about sixty."

He yawned. His eyes were red from all the driving, and he looked tired. "I don't know," he said. "The way I see it, this may be my last shot. If it isn't happening, I might just try to get into something respectable."

"Like Hal?" This was a joke with us. Hal was in insurance, and we had a lot of fun at his expense. Both of us thought insurance was about the most boring thing you could possibly do, and that by marrying Hal my mother had not so much found a mate as taken out a policy. Actually though, I kind of liked him. He never tried to be my father, he was just Hal. He left me alone when I didn't want to be bothered, and he was an incredible cook.

"Exactly like Hal. How do you think I'd look in a suit and tie?" He picked up his glasses and pointed them at me, businesslike. "Let's talk coverage, sir," he said in his best salesman's voice. "You tell me you play in a band? Fine. Say one day you get up there on stage, put a hand on your guitar, the other on the microphone. And let's just say that system isn't properly grounded. In one blue flash you get zapped right into the next state. What about your wife? Your kids? Who's going to take care of them? The musicians' union? You say you're not in the union? Well let me tell you, I have here a little policy designed just for you. We call it the Guitar Player's Friend—providing all-purpose coverage for you and your loved ones, and it's issued by the Chuck Berry Mutual Accident and Life insurance company, a name you've known and trusted for years. Believe me, you don't want to plug in without it."

The waitress interrupted him with our food. I waved a french fry at him. "Brilliant," I said. "You could be rich."

"Yeah, maybe," he said modestly. "I'd like to think I'll be able to leave you something someday." He sipped his coffee.

"If you had all the money you could ever want, what would you do?"

I chewed and thought. "I don't know, I guess I'd buy about ten guitars, a small recording studio and some video equipment," I said.

He nodded. "And where would you live?"

"Hawaii maybe. The Swiss alps."

"Good choices," he said. "A little romantic, but you're supposed to be romantic at fifteen."

"So? What would you do?" I asked.

"I believe," he said, "I'd do exactly what I'm doing right now."

He was tired and didn't feel like driving much more, so we started looking around for a place to stay. Since we were in Vermont, he said, we ought to find one of those quaint country inns where you slept under thick goose down comforters and they served you up a big New England style breakfast in the morning. We must have spent an hour driving around trying to find one. Eventually we settled on a motor court called Traveller's Rest, with a blinking neon sign of a sheep jumping over the name. The parking lot was empty, and my dad kept shaking his head over the fact that the one time he actually wanted to spend some money he couldn't find a way to do it, but I was happy. This was much more the kind of place I imagined crashing for the night, and as for the rest of that stuff, it wasn't really cold enough for a down comforter, and I was never much on breakfasts.

Our room was hooked up with cable television, and I immediately found an old movie that looked good, a British vampire flick with lots of gore and women nearly tumbling out of their bodices. My dad spent ten minutes going back and forth to the car bringing in all his guitars. It seemed a little odd to me that he'd bothered to take every single one of them along, but I didn't say anything. This was a very big audition for him, and I figured he just needed extra confidence. He took a pint bottle of Chivas Regal out of his bag, went into the bathroom and returned with two tissue-wrapped glasses. I'd never had Chivas, but I remembered reading on some album cover that it was John Lee Hooker's favorite drink. I squinched over to make room for him on the bed, then took the glass he handed me. He turned the sound on the television down.

"Your mother called me last week," he said, after a moment. "She says you're messing up in school."

"That's not true." I told him. "Just one class. I'm getting B's in everything else. Anyhow, why should she call you?"

"She wants us to stop hanging around together so much, at least till your grades pick up."

We almost never talked about school, except in the most general way, and having him speak to me like this—father to son, when we were now hundreds of miles from home—seemed a kind of betrayal.

"That's stupid," I said.

He nodded.

"I hope that's what you told her."

"I didn't tell her anything," he said. "I wanted to talk to you first."

I was suddenly angry at my mother for trying to interfere so blatantly with my life, and behind my back, too. I wasn't a kid anymore. I had been thinking about calling her; just to let her know I was all right, but now I felt like letting her stew a little.

"You know," he said, lying back on the bed and crossing his legs, "she's probably right. You have a dad who's thirty-five years old and still kicking around the same town he grew up in, still trying to land a steady gig. Being with me isn't going to help you become CEO of General Motors."

"Come on," I said. "You're my dad." I sipped at my drink, which made my eyes water.

"All right," he said, his eyes studying. "I just wanted to make sure."

A question occurred to me. "Could she do something? Something legal, I mean?"

"I don't know," he said. "It's a possibility." He got up and went into the bathroom to pee.

I made a promise to myself that regardless of what happened, things would continue on between us the way they always had. It was hard to imagine my mother actually doing something so drastic, but taking off without her permission had already given me a sense of power. Things could be any way I wanted them to be, I thought. What were they going to do, put me under armed guard?

"How long do you think we'll stay in Montreal?" I asked when he came back.

He looked through the blinds out at the parking lot. "Not long. A couple of days, tops." Then he slapped a hand down on my leg. "What do you say we head out and see if there's any nightlife around here?"

I jumped up and turned off the set. "Yeah," I said. Though my dad worked regularly in them, I'd never been to a bar.

We drove around until we found a little roadside place called "Mother's" that had pick-up trucks parked outside and a flashing red Miller sign in the window. There were maybe twenty-five people inside, not counting the band—five bored-looking guys in checked shirts playing sleepy country tunes. The guitar player didn't look much older than me, in spite of an attempted mustache. When we walked in I immediately sensed hostility, but I just followed my dad. He walked to the bar, took a seat, ordered us drinks and helped himself to a handful of peanuts from a bowl they had out. I reached in and grabbed a couple too. The bartender pursed his lips and considered me for a moment, then shrugged and uncapped us two long neck bottles of Bud.

"Never order anything fancy in a strange bar," said my dad, tipping back his bottle. "First thing people notice about you in a place like this is what you're drinking."

I nodded. We sat for a while, just swigging beer. Then I got up to go to the bathroom, and when I got back he was in a conversation with a fat guy he introduced as Al. Al worked as a mechanic, he said. He had huge, grease-blackened hands.

"This your kid?" asked Al.

My dad smiled proudly and I stood there feeling like a prize hog. I wished I were still back in the motel room watching television.

"I got a kid," said Al. I waited for him to say something else, but for Al the statement was a complete thought, and he just turned and faced the bar.

The band shuddered to a halt and went on break, and my dad ordered a round of shots for them, digging into his stuffed wallet and tossing a twenty onto the bar. Then he left me and Al sitting together, went over and got talking to the guitarist and bass player. I thought about all the bars in our town where he'd played. He was always in trouble with the club owners for showing up late, or mixing up dates, but he could smooth-talk them and manage to get hired again regardless. His ability in this respect was legendary. One time he got himself booked into two different places with different bands on the same night, and rather than cancel, he did half of one gig, then drove to the other and finished up the night there, using me as an excuse. "You came down with a convenient case of the mumps," he explained the next day. "I could never have made it without you." For two days after that, I walked around faking a cough and trying to look weak, just in case someone should want to check out his story.

Al wasn't much of a talker, so I drank at my beer and tried to pretend that hanging around in a bar was the most natural thing in the world for me. I counted the bottles of liquor lined up next to the cash register.

"Jimi," said my dad, coming over and poking me in the side. "We're going to sit in next set. What do you say?"

I looked into his eyes to see if he was kidding. I played a little guitar, but not very well, and never in front of people. The prospect terrified me, and I could see he was serious. "You go ahead," I said. "I'll watch."

"Come on. You play rhythm and I'll play lead. We'll do some blues. You can do that." He smiled encouragingly at me.

"I can't," I said. "Really."

"Sure you can," he told me.

I felt something close to panic, but at the same time it didn't seem that I had any choice. They had an extra guitar on stage for me, and the band's guitarist handed his over to my dad. When he did that he gave me a little smile that made the few dark hairs spread out on his upper lip. I took it as a sign of encouragement and plugged in. My dad called out "Red House," a Hendrix tune he knew I knew, and started playing. I tried to follow along, but after a few seconds I realized something was off.

My guitar was tuned a peculiar way. The chords I formed were one disaster after another, and my dad kept giving me furious looks, as if I was deliberately screwing around. Everything I played came out weird. He leaned over and shouted something to me that I could not hear above the music. I could see the band's guitarist leaning against the bar, laughing. I did the only thing I could think of. I stopped playing. Or rather, I pretended to play, damping the strings with my left hand so that no sound came out. My dad shook his head, turned away and began to sing.

He was really on. Toward the end he picked up an empty Budweiser bottle and ran it along the strings for a slide. I mimed along, numb, waiting for it to be over. We got hoots of approval and applause, but I barely heard them in my rush to get off.

The band's guitarist said something sarcastic to me as he took the instrument out of my hands. I jumped down, ignoring the amusement in his eyes, and went and stood next to the shuffleboard table while my dad talked to some of the locals—bearded men in checked wool jackets who clapped him on the back and offered to buy him drinks. Finally he came over to me.

"Let's go," I said.

It was cold in the parking lot, the air smelling of pine, the muted sounds of the bar mixing with the swell and hush of the wind in the trees. My dad walked me to the car and unlocked it.

"It was in open tuning," he said, finally. "Set up for slide."

"Yeah?" I said. "How was I supposed to know that?"

"You know about open tuning. All you had to do was think."

"I *couldn't* think!" I practically shouted. "Nothing sounded right and I didn't know what to do!"

"So what?" he said. "You just quit? You can't let yourself get beat like that."

"I didn't."

"Well, what do you call it?" He was glaring at me, and I could see that he was really upset about this, more so even than I was.

"I didn't quit," I said quietly. "I stayed up there with you."

We drove in a silence that I was afraid to break; the longer it went on the more permanent it felt. He wouldn't look at me. He was speeding too, I noticed, but I wasn't going to say anything. Then, about a mile from our motel he got pulled over by the cops.

As the officer shined his flashlight into our faces, I thought about the note he'd left. If my mother really had reported us to the police, this was probably it. I wondered what, if anything, they could do to him. I suspected he could get in a lot of trouble. Mostly though, I was worried he might not get to the audition, and that it would somehow be my fault. I sat frozen in anticipation, the cold night air flowing against my face from the open window, hoping as hard as I could for nothing bad to happen.

"Been doing a little drinking tonight?" asked the policeman as he examined my dad's license.

"Yes sir," he said. "Two beers. But I'm sober."

The cop pointed his flashlight in my face. "Who's that?"

"My son."

"Is that right?" He turned the light away from me and back at my dad. "Taking a little vacation are you?"

"You might say that."

"O.K., out of the car."

I had to sit for ten minutes while they ran him through a series of tasks to determine whether he was drunk. It was hard to watch. He walked a straight line four times, and counted backwards from fifty twice. All the while, another cop sat behind us, just a silhouette under the flashing blue light, speaking into his radio. They were checking on us, I knew. They didn't believe he was my father.

Finally, they wrote out a ticket and let us go. Just like that. This seemed incredible luck to me, and as soon as we were back underway, I let out a little whoop.

"Man," I said. "That was close."

But he still wasn't talking. In fact, he wouldn't even look at me. I wanted to tell him it didn't matter, to just forget it, but I couldn't. He didn't say anything at all until we got back to the motel. He put out a hand and tugged at the top of my head, then ran it down the back of my neck.

"You could use a haircut," he said.

When I woke the next morning, he was in the bathroom, shaving. I went and leaned against the door, watching him slide the razor carefully along the contours of his throat. He put a finger on his nose and pushed it comically to one side to get at his upper lip, turned and made a face at me. I liked seeing him shave. Getting my toothbrush, I fought him for some sink space. When he pushed back, I pushed harder, then scooped water out of the sink and splashed him. He dropped the razor, picked up the can of shaving cream and advanced toward me, his face still spotted with islands of foam. I ran, but he cornered me by the television, where he emptied half the can onto my head before I managed to wrestle it out of his hands. We stood there for a while, the two of us covered in shaving cream, laughing like a couple of kids. Then he took the can from my hands, flipped it once in the air and went back into the bathroom.

We reloaded the car and checked out. He paid cash for the room and asked the guy at the desk where we could get a good breakfast. The guy recommended a place about three miles away that turned out to be one of those country-style inns we'd been hoping to find the night before, and had in fact driven right past. We were both starved, and my dad told me to order a dream breakfast—anything I thought I could possibly eat. I had four eggs, home fries, sausages, waffles, toast, orange juice and coffee. He had steak and eggs with fried onions. The waitress looked a little hassled bringing out all that food—there was barely room for the plates—but we got a kick out of being so extravagant, and we tipped her heavily when we were through. After all, it wasn't our money.

We hit the road about eleven, windows open, tape deck turned up full. We sang along with old rock songs, and I beat out rhythms by banging one hand on the glove compartment and the other against the roof of the car. It was a perfect day to be driving, and north seemed the only direction possible. The Buick's big engine hummed powerfully in front of us, and even the air tasted like Canada—cool and fresh and full of promise.

"Hey," I said to him. "What do you say after Montreal we just keep on going? We could set a record. First station wagon to reach the North Pole."

"Bad idea," he said, adjusting his glasses with his forefinger.

"Why?"

"Because. Too much competition. The North Pole is swarming with guitarists already."

I kept quiet.

"Sure." He closed his eyes for a moment. "They've got this little town up there. It's jointly owned by all the major record companies."

"Not a very pleasant place to live," I said.

"That's the whole point, it's a miserable place to live." He reached over and turned the stereo down. " 'Bluestown,' " he said. "Most of the greats are up there, on salary, just their time. Muddy Waters, Jimi Hendrix, Duane Allman, Elmore James. All of them hanging out, drinking, jamming and trying to keep warm."

I forced a laugh, but I wondered. Sometimes he seemed to have no notion at all of how old I was. Or even that I was there at all. "So what you're saying is that they're actually still alive?" I asked.

"That's exactly what I'm saying. Where do you think they keep getting those 'newly discovered' tapes from? The blues wasn't selling, so they figured this would be a good way to stir up interest. And let me tell you something, a couple of years from now the world is going to be in for one hell of a surprise. Because they're coming back, all of them."

"Return of the Blues Guitarists," I said in my best coming-attractions voice. "When is this going to happen?"

He shrugged his shoulders. "Who knows? When we're ready for them, I guess. When everyone has had enough of the crap they play on the radio."

"Bluestown," I said, flipping through the road atlas. "You know, it's not here on the map."

"It's there," he said. "Trust me. You just go to Chicago, then head due north."

"But," I pointed out, "the North Pole is due north of everywhere, not just Chicago."

"Hey," he said. "Don't argue with your father."

I nodded off for a while, imagining a town built entirely of ice, with fur-bundled shapes walking up and down the streets carrying guitar cases. I kept thinking, how do I know these people are who they say they are if I can't see their faces? Then we got off the highway and I woke up. We were a little south of St. Johnsbury. My dad said he wanted to take a few minutes and look at a typical New England town. The place was called Denton, and it was truly quaint: tree-lined streets, big old houses with well-kept yards, two neat little white-steepled churches, only a couple of blocks apart. It was one of those picture-postcards of a town, and I thought it probably didn't look any different now than it had fifty years ago. I couldn't imagine what people there did for a living, but everyone we saw looked reasonably well-off. We drove up and down its few streets, looking at the houses, and just enjoying the simplicity of the place. It seemed that everything here was exactly the way it ought to be. In the center of town, he pulled over by the bus station and put the car in neutral.

"How about a couple of candy bars before we get going?" he said.

I was still stuffed from breakfast, and I couldn't imagine that he was actually hungry again, but I said sure and hopped out of the car. He stuck his hand out the window with a five dollar bill in it. I took the money and went inside.

It was a tiny bus station, just a window, two benches and a couple of vending machines. The guy at the window was out of singles, and I waited while he counted the whole five out in quarters, nickels and dimes. Then I bought two Snickers bars. With them in my hand, I stepped back out into the bright sunlight.

He was already gone. I could see the tailgate of the station wagon bouncing away from me down the street in the distance. I stood there watching him go, thinking that any moment now he would turn around and come back. It had to be a joke. But he kept going until the car disappeared over a crest.

I stared after him down the street. I was standing alone in the middle of a tiny Vermont town with two chocolate bars in my hand and no idea what to do next. Then I stuck my hand in my pocket and felt the wad of money. He had slipped it there somehow without my noticing, and when I took it out I counted nearly seven hundred dollars, most of it in fifties and twenties. I suddenly felt so strange I sat down right where I was on the curb.

It took a little while before I managed to collect myself. Then I walked up and down the main street of Denton, Vermont, looking into shop windows, kicking at loose stones on the street. I opened one of the candy bars and took a bite, but dropped the rest of it in a trashcan. I took out the roll of money again, fanned through it bitterly, and a small slip of yellow paper fell out from between two of the fifties. Picking it up, I saw that it was a withdrawal slip for just over nine hundred dollars from my father's bank, and on it in a teller's handwriting were the words "Account closed."

I stood for a while feeling the sun on my face, looking up at a solid blue sky that extended, unbroken, right up to the Canadian border and beyond. He hadn't planned on coming back. There was no audition. There had only been, for a brief while, an idea about the two of us starting over again someplace else, and maybe this time getting it right. I thought I understood what it felt like to look at your own future and see nothing but disappointment and failure stretching out like an endless series of clouds. The thing was, if he'd asked, I would have kept going. Taking all the change I had in my pockets, I began feeding the parking meters of downtown Denton, Vermont, pumping each one hard until it would take no more, then moving on to the next. I bought myself a lot of time, but after a while, I ran out of coins. Then I stepped back into the dark little bus station and paid for a one-way ticket home.

"Bluestown" Discussion

1. Take a close look at the first scene in the story, in which the father picks the son up at school. What immediate clues do we get about the father's character?
2. What details early in the story give us a hint that the father is not going to come through for the narrator?
3. The narrator describes the roadside diner this way: "It was . . . somehow not quite real . . . . It was someone's idea of what a diner should have looked like—lots of chrome and mirrors and a big, colorful jukebox." How does this description apply to the narrator's relationship with his father?
4. Why do you suppose the father likes to joke about Hal?
5. The narrator and his father look for a "quaint country inn" and end up in a motor court. How does this turn of luck reinforce the events of the story?

6. Why does his father's mention of school seem like a "betrayal" to the narrator?
7. Think about the scene in the bar—when the narrator can't play the guitar with his father. Why is this scene so important to the story? What does it tell us about the true nature of this relationship?
8. How does the title, "Bluestown," further illuminate the true nature of this relationship?
9. Why do you suppose the father chooses a quaint New England town in which to leave his son?
10. Do you think the narrator will turn out like his father? Why or why not?

Suggestion for Writing

We are sometimes disappointed by people we love because it is from them we expect the most. Write a short story about disappointment in a relationship. Try to infuse it with the kind of "telling" detail that Becker uses in "Bluestown."

Tickits

by Paul Milenski

(First appeared in Quarterly West*)*

Here is an example—a perfect example—of the "short short" story, in which an entire life is revealed in a few hundred words. Although we spend very little time with Toby, we come to understand him, empathize with him, and learn from him.

About the Author

As a child, PAUL MILENSKI wrote in a mix of Polish (his first language) and English. Since then he has published over a hundred stories world-wide. "Tickits" alone has been translated into several languages and is featured in the school curriculum of countries as far away as New Zealand and China. Of Toby, the main character in "Tickits," Paul writes: "He is based on a real-life character, a retarded woman who, each day, took to railing against the injustices of society by writing out little colored slips of paper, handing them to passers-by." Paul is a former English teacher and school superintendent who quit his educational career at age forty to fulfill his dream of becoming a writer.

Toby Heckler placed the slip of yellow paper under the windshield wiper of the black Oldsmobile that straddled two parking spaces. On the yellow paper Toby had printed in red ink "PRAKING MISTEAK" and signed his name "TOBY" in a childish-looking hand. He snapped the cover on his Pilot Razor Point, slipped the pen over his ear, put the pad of yellow papers in his jacket pocket. He moved down Main Street, his chin held high, his sneakers spanking white from Baby's Liquid Shoe Polish.

As Toby passed Thom McAn, he looked in the window, caught the reflection of his sneakers, looked down at them, moved his toes inside. He straightened the pen on his ear, patted the pad of yellow papers in his pocket, moved along. People stared at Toby; he kept his chin high.

Near the First National Bank two elderly ladies waited for the bus. They stood in the middle of the sidewalk away from the curb. Toby pulled out his pad, slipped the pen off his ear, held the cap with his teeth. He printed slowly, meticulously, then handed one of the ladies the slip, "TO MUSH IN WAY" signed "TOBY." He secured his instruments, walked along as before. The two ladies examined the slip of paper, moved closer to the curb.

At the intersection of Main and South the pedestrian crossing light shone bright orange, "DON'T WALK." Traffic moved, people stood on the curb. A man with a pin-striped suit and briefcase stepped off the curb, was about to sneak across between cars. Toby began to reach for his pad. The cars closed together; the man stepped back to the curb. Toby brought his hand back. When the green light read "WALK," Toby and the man crossed. The man went into a shop. Toby waited for him, handed him a slip as he came out, "ALLMOST WALKD."

Patrolman McVee stood in front of Charlie's Tobacco Shop; McVee's badge number was 635. Toby stopped, stood next to him. McVee looked over.

"How's it going, Toby?" McVee said.

Toby pulled out his pad, showed it to McVee.

"Lots of business, eh, Toby?"

Toby put his pad back, nodded. His eyes rolled, looked tortured.

"Yes, Toby, it's a bitch," McVee said.

Toby looked at McVee's shoes. Except for a single smudge they were shiny, black. Toby bent down, rubbed off the smudge with his hand.

"Thanks, Toby," McVee said.

Toby caught McVee's eye, looked down at his own sneakers.

"Very nice, Toby. Spiffy," McVee said.

Toby raised his chin again, moved along.

Before the rain came, Toby had used up half his pad. Near Mario's Grinders there was a dog tied to a parking meter; he had wrapped his leash tightly around the pole. Toby stuck a slip under his collar, "TYED WORNG." Toby walked into the YMCA, handed the man at the desk a slip, "Y BORKEN." On a Park Square bench a man ate a candy bar; he threw his wrapper down. Toby handed him the wrapper and a slip, "PAPUR ON GARSS." The man walked away throwing both papers down. Toby caught up to him, gave him all the papers and another slip, "NOT LISSENING." The man said "Christ," put all the papers in his pocket.

The rain began to wet Toby's slips, blot his ink. He put everything away, looked up at the sky, rolled his eyes.

By the time he got back to Main and South, it was raining hard. A car moved through the intersection, splashed dirty water on his sneakers. Toby walked quickly down South, cut through the alley between Sam's Auto Supplies and Blue Arc Welding, avoided puddles on Mill, moved along the flood control wall on River, came to his bungalow, entered.

Inside there were smells of cabbage, cigarette smoke, spilt alcohol. The entry was dark, lit intermittently with a pale light from the television. He knew his mother lay on the sofa, smoking, drinking, surrounded by TV magazines. The sofa with a large hump cast a shadow on the wall.

Toby took off his sneakers, carried them up the stairs.

His mother turned her head, "Toby, is that you?" Her voice was raspy, tired. But Toby was already in his room, the door closed, Baby's Liquid Shoe Polish in front of him on the floor.

His mother moved to the bottom of the stairs. She coughed, yelled, "Toby!"

Toby opened the door, showed himself to his mother.

She held a cigarette and a drink. "Toby, you could've been a goddamn burglar sneaking around me like that!" Toby closed the door, reached under his bed.

"Toby, you goddamn nut!"

Toby pulled out a shoebox. On the cover it read, "MUTHERS TICKITS."

Toby wrote three slips: "TO MUSH SOMKING," "TO MUSH DIRNKING," "TOO MUSH YELING." He placed the slips in the box. Then, before he put the box away, he wrote one more slip in his largest letters: "ERVYTHING WORNG!"

With the box safely under his bed, Toby sat on the floor, bit his tongue, went to polishing his sneakers spanking white.

"Tickits" Discussion

1. Why do you suppose the story contains such exact detail: the bank is the First National Bank, the pen a Pilot Razor Point, the store window a Thom McAn window, the shoe polish Baby's Liquid Shoe Polish. All the streets are exactly identified, too, as well as other businesses and stores. How does this exactness of detail describe Toby to us?

2. What do we know about Toby's life at home?
3. What do you suppose Toby looks like?
4. What do you think is wrong with Toby?
5. Why does Toby write tickets?
6. How would you react if somebody like Toby handed you a "tickit"?
7. If you could get away with handing out tickets the way Toby does, to whom would you give them, and for what offense?
8. How would the story change if all the tickets were spelled correctly?
9. Do you think Toby will ever show his mother her tickets? Why or why not?
10. Do you like Toby? Why or why not? What can we learn from Toby?

Suggestion for Writing

The "short short" story has no specific definition but is generally accepted as being a story that is complete within one to six pages. The operative word is *complete.* It is relatively easy to write six pages of fiction, much harder to infuse those six pages with a beginning, middle, and end—in other words, a story that seems full and satisfying. In "Tickits" we are given only a few moments of Toby's life, yet the story seems done at the end—as if we have learned something about Toby and the way he creates meaning in his discouraging life.

See if you can write a similar "slice of life"—just a few pages, or paragraphs—and make it seem whole. Try to imitate the techniques that make "Tickits" work: a sense of *place* (in Toby's case, the small town, the kind policeman, the tolerant "offenders"); the telling detail (Toby's polished sneakers, his rolled eyes, his Pilot Razor Point pen, the comically misspelled, uppercase words); and the revelation at the end that there is more to Toby's actions than meets the eye.

Feeding the Piranha

by Pamela Painter

(*First appeared in* The Atlantic Monthly)

Who are the children and who are the adults? It is not always easy to tell. This story, by turns funny and poignant, lets the reader in on how it feels to be a kid stuck between divorced parents.

About the Author

Photo Credit: Eric Rasmussen
© 1990

PAMELA PAINTER began writing stories when she was teaching high school in New Hampshire. When her students complained about their story-writing assignment, she agreed to write a story herself. It became her first published story. Since then she has published an award-winning collection, GETTING TO KNOW THE WEATHER, and appeared in such magazines as *The Atlantic Monthly*, *Harper's*, and *Mademoiselle*. She received a "distinguished story" mention in THE BEST AMERICAN SHORT STORIES 1990. Pamela recently co-authored WHAT IF? EXERCISES FOR FICTION WRITERS with Anne Bernays (HarperCollins).

Our father waits until we have picked up our duffels and left the San Diego airport to ask if we've had our teeth cleaned lately. "Josh?" he asks me. I say no, not lately. "Finny?" My sister says she thinks she has a cavity in one of her back teeth, either top right or bottom right. Her tongue visits the elected spots, probing for confirmation. Dad nods, satisfied that this will be a good visit. And doctor's checkups? I disappoint him with my required physical for football this fall, but Finny's shake of her head assures him that where our mother's neglect is concerned, nothing has changed. Not that he's about to pay for any of this. Finny and I exchange glances as we pull into his apartment complex. It's all cement except for stunted palm trees in cracked clay pots and patches of bright-green grass, one per apartment, each with its own sprinkler whirring away. Nothing else moves. The pool is smaller than it sounded on the phone.

Dad throws our duffels and books into his empty extra bedroom, beside the sleeping bags he borrowed for us. I explore the tiny balcony baking in the California sun while Finny assesses the fridge. The balcony is three feet by six feet. A rusted hibachi sits on bricks at one end, like an abandoned altar. Back inside, Finny slams the door of the fridge. "Guess we better go shopping," she says.

We gather in the living room, where Dad explains about his temporary lack of employment and how he didn't want to ruin our first visit in a year by looking for job. His time is ours. He spreads his arms expansively in a gesture I remember. "So, Josh, how much money did your mother give you?" he asks. We pool our money on the oak table from the Chicago family room. I have fifty dollars. Finny has thirty. Dad has twelve dollars and nineteen cents. As the coins plunk down, the nineteen cents makes me feel guilty.

But not guilty enough to mention the other fifty bucks in my back pocket or the twenty in Finny's new Madonna purse.

The money on the table comes to $92.19. Dad scoops it all into his hand and puts it in the pocket of his jogging pants. We head off to our first meal, at Burger King—my favorite restaurant. There Dad catches us up on his latest jobs and why they didn't work out.

"You have to be able to cut your losses," he says. "Your mother's probably still teaching. Stuck in the same rut."

"Yeah," Finny says, "she'll never quit."

Later we shop for eggs, milk, ketchup, hamburger, and bread.

"Your mother still making that fancy food?" he asks.

"I don't eat it," I tell him, rolling my eyes at the thought of the shrimp curry, the coq au vin, the cold pasta salads, that I'm gladly missing. "I eat cereal," I say, and dump more ketchup on my fries.

Dad and I run three miles every morning while Finny stays in her sleeping bag and reads *Playboys*. They have great interviews, Dad says. Before we run, he stretches out in front of a mirror, seriously bending, pulling, reaching. I do what he does right behind him in the mirror. He's in better shape than I am—except for losing a little hair. He asks if Mom is still fat, and I say yes, that all her skirts have stretch waistbands. But, Finny says, expensive clothes hide it well. I add that her new husband probably doesn't notice, because his nose is always in some book. Dad laughs; no books are cluttering up his house.

Dad arranges for courts every day that his old club has extras—usually at 6:00 in the morning or 11:00 at night. Dad plays Finny first, then me. "You keeping up with your tennis?" he asks. "Pretty much," I say. Then I tell him about Mom's refusal to send me to tennis camp last summer, even though it would have guaranteed me first place on the team.

Finny says Mom held back because she had just bought a new computer. "Still got her priorities mixed up," Dad says.

We meet the girlfriends on different nights. Girlfriend Number One is closer to my age than his. She has great boobs and the sort of overhead smash that in a couple of years would get me into college. We play doubles and go out to Burger King. Then we go to her place for a sleepover. Dad packed our sleeping bags in the back of the car, just in case.

Girlfriend Number Two shows Finny how to make up her eyes with black eyeliner and colors like purple and plum and apricot. She puts lipstick on her with a pencil. The next day they go out to the Hacienda Mall to have Finny's ears pierced. Finny comes back with two gold circles in each ear.

Girlfriend Number Three cooks real Chinese food and shows us how to use chopsticks. Her apartment complex has a trampoline next to the pool. We take turns jumping and falling and reclining and jumping up again. Working on our appetites, Dad says.

"We play hard and sleep late out here," Dad says. "Your mom ever take time off?"

"Just for Scrabble or chess," Finny says.

"But it's no fun, 'cause she doesn't let anybody talk."

Dad has an invitation to move in with any of the three. So which one will it be? he asks, later in the week, when we are back at his place, sitting beside the empty pool, which is being repainted. I vote for Number One and Finny votes for Number Two.

"But what do we do about Number Three?" Dad asks. "No doubt your mother would have some well-chosen words on the subject. Does she still talk most of the time with her hands on her hips?" We both picture it and say yes.

Our grandmother calls, from a little town north of L.A. Finny figures out that we last saw her eight or nine years ago. I remember Skippy, her dog, a dachshund with scabby hair who wouldn't stop playing fetch. I remember the musical toilet seat that played "She'll Be Coming Round the Mountain When She Comes."

Our grandmother tells Dad that she and Grandpap won't be able to make it down from the mountains to see us this time, but to say hello for them. We'll all get together at a big reunion next time for sure. He passes this along to us. To her he says, "The kids, they are sooooo biggo. Mucho biggo." To us he says, "Your grandmother wants to know if you get the letters and cards she sends or does your mother throw them away?"

"I don't remember getting anything," Finny says. "What's the name of the town they live in?"

Before long we have to pack. Finny searches the car for our plane tickets while I throw my clothes in a duffel, sniffing to decide what to wear home. We have run out of clean clothes. A few things I can't find. Dad watches us pack. "Can't your mother buy you enough clothes to get through a week?" Dad asks. He has an unending supply of jogging pants and tennis shorts.

"Mom makes us do laundry instead," I say. "She goes nuts on Clorox and Spray 'n Wash and Bounce."

"You name it and we learn to use it," Finny says.

We stop at Burger King on the way to the airport. I order double fries, to get the baseball cards, and pie. "Hold it on the apple pie," Dad says. "We're almost out of money." Finny keeps checking her makeup in her new Madonna compact. She's not so good with the lipstick pencil yet. I'm wearing a T-shirt from the Del Mar Tennis Club.

At the airport Dad talks the woman at the security gate into letting him walk his only kids to the boarding area. She laughs us through. Dad's face is red, his voice husky. He asks if we missed our mother and we say no. He asks, Do you ever miss me? and we say yes.

In Boston it's raining, and the fog makes our plane late. We get a cab home. Mom is making curried shrimp and banana raita for dinner. She hugs us, and here it comes. "Did you miss me?" she asks. We say yes. She wipes Finny's lipstick off her cheek and steps back. "What happened to your eyes?" she asks Finny. "You look like a raccoon." My stepfather glances up from his book and says hello. He says hello again, and then goes back to where his finger marks his place.

Mom follows us to our bedrooms to collect the dirty clothes she is sure we came home with. "So how's your father doing?" she asks. Finny tells her Dad is almost bald and wears jogging suits absolutely everywhere. "He still wears his Princeton ring," I say. "He lost the old one at the beach last year and had to order another from Balfour's."

"So, what did you do in sunny California?" Mom asks, hands on her hips.

"There isn't a book in the house," Finny says. "Just his old *Playboys*."

"Went running, played a lot of tennis at cheap times like six A.M.," I say.

"Did you see your grandparents?" Mom asks.

"They were too busy," Finny says, "as usual. They're probably pissed we don't cash their piddling five-dollar Christmas and birthday checks, but I knew she was on the phone because Dad was talking baby talk."

Mom giggles as if remembering. "Any wedding plans?" she asks.

I say he seems to have more than one girlfriend. "One's only a few years older than me."

"I," Mom says.

"The other girlfriends are closer to your age," I tell her.

"He takes turns seeing them. It's Dad who calls them girls."

Mom says, "Well, nothing's changed."

My sister peers in the mirror at her earlobes and asks Mom to check them out. She's sure the holes are unevenly punched; one looks red and yucky. Mom gets close. "Jesus, you had a surgical procedure done at the mall," Mom says.

Later Mom ladles out shrimp curry while I pour cereal into a bowl.

"Does your father have a job?" she asks.

"Yeah, jogging's hard work," Finny says. She counts up the meals at Burger King, describes the fridge—empty except for ketchup. She tells Mom that once again we had to contribute our money to expenses, because once again Dad doesn't have a job.

"But we didn't give him all the money this time," Finny says. "If I can walk dogs, he can get a job."

"Fat chance," I say. I tell Mom I didn't even ask him about sending me to tennis camp. I was afraid he'd suggest I leave my extra racquet there for him to use. Mom is putting two and two together with the past twenty years.

"Do you think we'll be able to count on any money for college?" she asks.

"Not a chance," my sister says, "but the next time we go out there, we'll steal his car."

I tell Mom, by then he probably won't have a car.

"*Feeding the Piranha*" Discussion

1. Notice how subtly the author reveals the way this family operates. Reread the opening paragraph: What insights does Josh, the narrator, have about his father?

2. "The pool is smaller than it sounded on the phone," Josh observes when he first arrives at his father's. He also observes the smallness of the balcony and other disappointments. How do these observations reveal the character of the father?

3. Why do you suppose Josh and Finny tell their father unflattering things about their mother?
4. How does Josh feel about his father's girlfriends? How do we know this?
5. Why do you suppose the father keeps asking questions about the mother?
6. Why do you suppose Finny pretends never to have gotten the grandmother's letters?
7. When Josh and Finny arrive home again, we see the other side of their life. Just as the opening paragraph gives us insights about their father, the opening of the last section gives us insights about life at their mother's. What do we learn?
8. Do you like Josh and Finny? Why or why not? Is there anything they should do differently?
9. Do you like the mother? The father? Why? How would you like them to change?
10. What role do Josh and Finny play in their parents' lives?

Suggestion for Writing

This story is written by a woman, yet the narrator is a boy. Try writing a scene or story using a narrator of the opposite sex.

What Means Switch

by Gish Jen

(First appeared in The Atlantic Monthly*)*

This funny, tender story, set in the mid-sixties, features a young, inventive Chinese-American narrator, Mona Chang, whose first brush with love brings her face to face with her identity. Who am I? she seems to ask. It is a question we all face, but for Mona the answer is complicated by her American roots, her Chinese heritage, her Japanese boyfriend, and her Jewish neighborhood.

About the Author

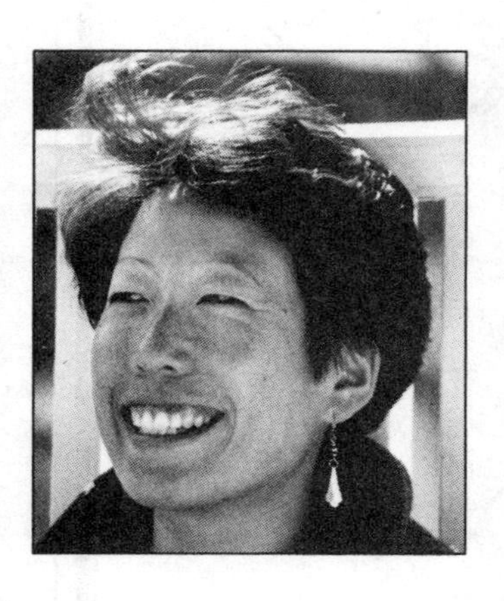

GISH JEN has published in numerous magazines and anthologies, including THE BEST AMERICAN SHORT STORIES 1988, NEW WORLDS OF LITERATURE, and *The Atlantic Monthly*. She is also the author of a novel, TYPICAL AMERICAN (Houghton Mifflin). Gish has received support from the National Endowment for the Arts, the Massachusetts Artists' Foundation, the Michener Foundation, and the Radcliffe Bunting Institute.

There we are, nice Chinese family—father, mother, two born-here girls. Where should we live next? My parents slide the question back and forth like a cup of ginseng neither one wants to drink. Until finally it comes to them, what they really want is a milkshake (chocolate) and to go with it a house in Scarsdale. What else? The broker tries to hint: the neighborhood, she says. Moneyed. Many delis. Meaning rich and Jewish. But someone has sent my parents a list of the top ten schools nation-wide (based on the opinion of selected educators and others) and so *many-deli* or not we nestle into a Dutch colonial on the Bronx River Parkway. The road's windy where we are, very charming; drivers miss their turns, plow up our flower beds, then want to use our telephone. "Of course," my mom tells them, like it's no big deal, we can replant. We're the type to adjust. You know—the lady drivers weep, my mom gets out the Kleenex for them. We're a bit down the hill from the private plane set, in other words. Only in our dreams do our jacket zippers jam, what with all the lift tickets we have stapled to them, Killington on top of Sugarbush on top of Stowe, and we don't even know where the Virgin Islands are—although certain of us do know that virgins are like priests and nuns, which there were a lot more of in Yonkers, where we just moved from, than there are here.

This is my first understanding of class. In our old neighborhood everybody knew everything about virgins and non-virgins, not to say the technicalities of staying in-between. Or almost everybody, I should say; in Yonkers I was the laugh-along type. Here I'm an expert.

"You mean the man . . . ?" Pig-tailed Barbara Gugelstein spits a mouthful of Coke back into her can. "That is *so* gross!"

Pretty soon I'm getting popular for a new girl, the only problem is Danielle Meyers, who wears blue mascara and has gone steady with two boys. "How do *you* know," she starts to ask, proceeding to edify us all with how she French-kissed one boyfriend and just regular kissed another. ("Because, you know, he had braces.") We hear about his rubber bands, how once one popped right into her mouth. I begin to realize I need to find somebody to kiss too. But how?

Luckily, I just about then happen to tell Barbara Gugelstein I know karate. I don't know why I tell her this. My sister Callie's the liar in the family; ask anybody. I'm the one who doesn't see why we should have to hold our heads up. But for some reason I tell Barbara Gugelstein I can make my hands like steel by thinking hard. "I'm not supposed to tell anyone," I say.

The way she backs away, blinking, I could be the burning bush.

"I can't do bricks," I say—a bit of expectation management. "But I can do your arm if you want." I set my hand in chop position.

"Uhh, it's okay," she says. "I know you can, I saw it on TV last night."

That's when I recall that I too saw it on TV last night—in fact, at her house. I rush on to tell her I know how to get pregnant with tea.

"With *tea?*"

"That's how they do it in China."

She agrees that China is an ancient and great civilization that ought to be known for more than spaghetti and gunpowder. I tell her I know Chinese. "*Be-yeh fa-foon,*" I say. "*Shee-veh. Ji nu.*" Meaning, "Stop acting crazy. Rice gruel. Soy sauce." She's impressed. At lunch the next day, Danielle Meyers and Amy Weinstein and Barbara's crush, Andy Kaplan, are all impressed too. Scarsdale is a liberal town, not like Yonkers, where the Whitman Road Gang used to throw crabapple mash at my sister Callie and me and tell us it would make our eyes stick shut. Here we're like permanent exchange students. In another ten years, there'll be so many Orientals we'll turn into Asians; a Japanese grocery will buy out that one deli too many. But for now, the mid-sixties, what with civil rights on TV, we're not so much accepted as embraced. Especially by the Jewish part of town—which, it turns out, is not all of town at all. That's just an idea people have, Callie says, and lots of them could take us or leave us same as the Christians, who are nice too; I shouldn't generalize. So let me not generalize except to say that pretty soon I've been to so many bar and bas mitzvahs, I can almost say myself whether the kid chants like an angel or like a train conductor, maybe they could use him on the commuter line. At seder I know to forget the bricks, get a good pile of that mortar. Also I know what is schmaltz. I know that I am a goy. This is not why people like me, though. People like me because I do not need to use deodorant, as I demonstrate in the locker room before and after gym. Also, I can explain to them, for example, what is tofu (*der-voo*, we say at home). Their mothers invite me to taste-test their Chinese cooking.

"Very authentic." I try to be reassuring. After all, they're nice people, I like them. "De-lish." I have seconds. On the question of what we eat, though, I have to admit, "Well, no, it's different than that." I have thirds. "What my mom makes is home style, it's not in the cookbooks."

Not in the cookbooks! Everyone's jealous. Meanwhile, the big deal at home is when we have turkey pot pie. My sister Callie's the one introduced them—Mrs. Wilder's, they come in this green-and-brown box—and when we have them, we both get suddenly interested in helping out in the kitchen. You know, we stand in front of the oven and help them bake. Twenty-five minutes. She and I have a deal, though, to keep it secret from school, as everybody else thinks they're gross. We think they're a big improvement over authentic Chinese home cooking. Ox-tail soup—now that's gross. Stir-fried beef with tomatoes. One day I say, "You know, Ma, I have never seen a stir-fried tomato in any Chinese restaurant we have ever been in, ever."

"In China," she says, real lofty, "we consider tomatoes are a delicacy."

"Ma," I say. "Tomatoes are *Italian*."

"No respect for elders." She wags her finger at me, but I can tell it's just to try and shame me into believing her. "I'm tell you, tomatoes *invented* in China."

"*Ma*."

"Is true. Like noodles. Invented in China."

"That's not what they said in *school*."

"In *China*," my mother counters, "we also eat tomatoes uncooked, like apple. And in summertime we slice them, and put some sugar on top."

"Are you sure?"

My mom says of course she's sure, and in the end I give in, even though she once told me that China was such a long time ago, a lot of things she can hardly remember. She said sometimes she has trouble remembering her characters, that sometimes she'll be writing a letter, just writing along, and all of a sudden she won't be sure if she should put four dots or three.

"So what do you do then?"

"Oh, I just make a little sloppy."

"You mean you *fudge*?"

She laughed then, but another time, when she was showing me how to write my name, and I said, just kidding, "Are you sure that's the right number of dots now?" she was hurt.

"I mean, of course you know," I said. "I mean, *oy*."

Meanwhile, what *I* know is that in the eighth grade, what people want to hear does not include how Chinese people eat sliced tomatoes with sugar on top. For a gross fact, it just isn't gross enough. On the other hand, the fact that somewhere in China somebody eats or has eaten or once ate living monkey brains—now that's conversation.

"They have these special tables," I say, "kind of like a giant collar. With a hole in the middle, for the monkey's neck. They put the monkey in the collar, and then they cut off the top of its head."

"Whadda they use for cutting?"

I think. "Scalpels."

"*Scalpels?*" says Andy Kaplan.

"Kaplan, don't be dense," Barbara Gugelstein says. "The Chinese *invented* scalpels."

Once a friend said to me, You know, everybody is valued for something. She explained how some people resented being valued for their looks; others resented being valued for their money. Wasn't it still better to be beautiful and rich than ugly and poor, though? You should be just glad, she said, that you have something people value. It's like having a special talent, like being good at ice-skating, or opera-singing. She said, You could probably make a career out of it.

Here's the irony: I am.

Anyway. I am ad-libbing my way through eighth grade, as I've described. Until one bloomy spring day, I come in late to homeroom, and to my chagrin discover there's a new kid in class.

Chinese.

So what should I do, pretend to have to go to the girls' room, like Barbara Gugelstein the day Andy Kaplan took his ID back? I sit down; I am so cool I remind myself of Paul Newman. First thing I realize, though, is that no one looking at me is thinking of Paul Newman. The notes fly:

"*I* think he's cute."

"Who?" I write back. (I am still at an age, understand, when I believe a person can be saved by aplomb.)

"I don't think he talks English too good. Writes it either."

"Who?"

"They might have to put him behind a grade, so don't worry."

"He has a crush on you already, you could tell as soon as you walked in, he turned kind of orangish."

I hope I'm not turning orangish as I deal with my mail. I could use a secretary. The second round starts:

"What do you mean who? Don't be weird. Didn't you *see* him??? Straight back over your right shoulder!!!!"

I have to look; what else can I do? I think of certain tips I learned in Girl Scouts about poise. I cross my ankles. I hold a pen in my hand. I sit up as though I have a crown on my head. I swivel my head slowly, repeating to myself, *I* could be Miss America.

"Miss Mona Chang."

Horror raises its hoary head.

"Notes, please."

Mrs. Mandeville's policy is to read all notes aloud.

I try to consider what Miss America would do, and see myself, back straight, knees together, crying. Some inspiration. Cool Hand Luke, on the other hand, would, quick, eat the evidence. And why not? I should yawn as I stand up, and boom, the notes are gone. All that's left is to explain that it's an old Chinese reflex.

I shuffle up to the front of the room.

"One minute please," Mrs. Mandeville says.

I wait, noticing how large and plastic her mouth is.

She unfolds a piece of paper.

And I, Miss Mona Chang, who got almost straight A's her whole life except in math and conduct, am about to start crying in front of everyone.

I am delivered out of hot Egypt by the bell. General pandemonium. Mrs. Mandeville still has her hand clamped on my shoulder, though. And the next thing I know, I'm holding the new boy's schedule. He's standing next to me like a big blank piece of paper. "This is Sherman," Mrs. Mandeville says.

"Hello," I say.

"*Non how a*," I say.

I'm glad Barbara Gugelstein isn't there to see my Chinese in action.

"*Ji nu*," I say. "*Shee veh.*"

Later I find out that his mother asked if there were any other Orientals in our grade. She had him put in my class on purpose. For now, though, he looks at me as though I'm much stranger than anything else he's seen so far. Is this because he understands I'm saying "soy sauce rice gruel" to him or because he doesn't?

"Sher-man," he says finally.

I look at his schedule card. Sherman Matsumoto. What kind of name is that for a nice Chinese boy?

(Later on, people ask me how I can tell Chinese from Japanese. I shrug. You just kind of know, I say. *Oy!*)

Sherman's got the sort of looks I think of as pretty-boy. Monsignor-black hair (not monk brown like mine), bouncy. Crayola eyebrows, one with a round bald spot in the middle of it, like a golf hole. I don't know how anybody can think of him as orangish; his skin looks white to me, with pink triangles hanging down the front of his cheeks like flags. Kind of delicate-looking, but the only truly uncool thing about him is that his spiral notebook has a picture of a kitty cat on it. A big white fluffy one, with a blue ribbon above each perky little ear. I get much opportunity to view this, as all the poor kid understands about life in junior high school is that he should follow me everywhere. It's embarrassing. On the other hand, he's obviously even more miserable than I am, so I try not to say anything. Give him a chance to adjust. We communicate by sign language, and by drawing pictures, which he's better at than I am; he puts in every last detail, even if it takes forever. I try to be patient.

A week of this. Finally I enlighten him. "You should get a new notebook."

His cheeks turn a shade of pink you mostly only see in hyacinths.

"Notebook." I point to his. I show him mine, which is psychedelic, with big purple and yellow stick-on flowers. I try to explain he should have one like this, only without the flowers. He nods enigmatically, and the next day brings me a notebook just like his, except that this cat sports pink bows instead of blue.

"Pret-ty," he says. "You."

He speaks English! I'm dumbfounded. Has he spoken it all this time? I consider: Pretty. You. What does that mean? Plus actually, he's said *plit-ty*, much as my parents would; I'm assuming he means pretty, but maybe he means pity. Pity. You.

"Jeez," I say finally.

"You are wel-come," he says.

I decorate the back of the notebook with stick-on flowers, and hold it so that these show when I walk through the halls. In class I mostly keep my book open. After all, the kid's so new; I think I really ought to have a heart. And for a livelong day nobody notices.

Then Barbara Gugelstein sidles up. "Matching notebooks, huh?"

I'm speechless.

"First comes love, then comes marriage, and then come chappies in a baby carriage."

"Barbara!"

"Get it?" she says. "Chinese Japs."

"Bar-*bra*," I say to get even.

"Just make sure he doesn't give you any *tea*," she says.

Are Sherman and I in love? Three days later, I hazard that we are. My thinking proceeds this way: I think he's cute, and I think he thinks I'm cute. On the other hand, we don't kiss and we don't exactly have fantastic conversation. Our talks *are* getting better, though. We started out, "This is a book." "Book." "This is a chair." "Chair." Advancing to, "What is this?" "This is a book." Now, for fun, he tests me.

"What is this?" he says.

"This is a book," I say, as if I'm the one who has to learn how to talk.

He claps. "Good!"

Meanwhile, people ask me all about him, I could be his press agent.

"No, he doesn't eat raw fish."

"No, his father wasn't a kamikaze pilot."

"No, he can't do karate."

"Are you sure?" somebody asks.

Indeed he doesn't know karate, but judo he does. I am hurt I'm not the one to find this out; the guys know from gym class. They line up to be flipped, he flips them all onto the floor, and after that he doesn't eat lunch at the girls' table with me anymore. I'm more or less glad. Meaning, when he was there, I never knew what to say. Now that he's gone, though, I seem to be stuck at the "This is a chair" level of conversation. Ancient Chinese eating habits have lost their cachet; all I get are more and more questions about me and Sherman. "I dunno," I'm saying all the time. *Are* we going out? We do stuff, it's true. For example, I take him to the department stores, explain to him who shops in Alexander's, who shops in Saks. I tell him my family's the type that shops in Alexander's. He says he's sorry. In Saks he gets lost; either that, or else I'm the lost one. (It's true I find him calmly waiting at the front door, hands behind his back, like a guard.) I take him to the candy store. I take him to the bagel store. Sherman is crazy about bagels. I explain to him that Lender's is gross, he should get his bagels from the bagel store. He says thank you.

"Are you going steady?" people want to know.

How can we go steady when he doesn't have an ID bracelet? On the other hand, he brings me more presents than I think any girl's ever gotten before. Oranges. Flowers. A little bag of bagels. But what do they mean? Do they mean thank you, I enjoyed our trip; do they mean I like you; do they mean I decided I liked the Lender's better even if they are gross, you can have these? Sometimes I think he's acting on his mother's instructions. Also I know at least a couple of the presents were supposed to go to our teachers. He told me that once and turned red. I figured it still might mean something that he didn't throw them out.

More and more now, we joke. Like, instead of "I'm thinking," he always says, "I'm sinking," which we both think is so funny, that all either one of us has to do is pretend to be drowning and the other one cracks up. And he tells me things—for example, that there are electric lights everywhere in Tokyo now.

"You mean you didn't have them before?"

"Everywhere now!" He's amazed too. "Since Olympics!"

"Olympics?"

"1960," he says proudly, and as proof, hums for me the Olympic theme song. "You know?"

"Sure," I say, and hum with him happily. We could be a picture on a UNICEF poster. The only problem is that I don't really understand what the Olympics have to do with the modernization of Japan, any more than I get this other story he tells me, about that hole in his left eyebrow, which is from some time his father accidentally hit him with a lit cigarette. When Sherman was a baby. His father was drunk, having been out carousing; his mother was very mad but didn't say anything, just cleaned the whole house. Then his father was so ashamed he bowed to ask her forgiveness.

"Your mother cleaned the house?"

Sherman nods solemnly.

"And your father *bowed?*" I find this more astounding than anything I ever thought to make up. "That is so weird," I tell him.

"Weird," he agrees. "This I no forget, forever. *Father* bow to *mother!*"

We shake our heads.

As for the things he asks me, they're not topics I ever discussed before. Do I like it here? Of course I like it here, I was born here, I say. Am I Jewish? Jewish! I laugh. Oy! Am I American? "Sure I'm American," I say. "Everybody who's born here is American, and also some people who convert from what they were before. You could become American." But he says no, he could never. "Sure you could," I say. "You only have to learn some rules and speeches."

"But I Japanese," he says.

"You could become American anyway," I say. "Like I *could* become Jewish, if I wanted to. I'd just have to switch, that's all."

"But you Catholic," he says.

I think maybe he doesn't get what means switch.

I introduce him to Mrs. Wilder's turkey pot pies. "Gross?" he asks. I say they are, but we like them anyway. "Don't tell anybody." He promises. We bake them, eat them. While we're eating, he's drawing me pictures.

"This American," he says, and he draws something that looks like John Wayne. "This Jewish," he says, and draws something that looks like the Wicked Witch of the West, only male.

"I don't think so," I say.

He's undeterred. "This Japanese," he says, and draws a fair rendition of himself. "This Chinese," he says, and draws what looks to be another fair rendition of himself.

"How can you tell them apart?"

"This way," he says, and he puts the picture of the Chinese so that it is looking at the pictures of the American and the Jew. The Japanese faces the wall. Then he draws another picture, of a Japanese flag, so that the Japanese has that to contemplate. "Chinese lost in department store," he says. "Japanese know how go." For fun, he then takes the Japanese flag and fastens it to the refrigerator door with magnets. "In school, in ceremony, we this way," he explains, and bows to the picture.

When my mother comes in, her face is so red that with the white wall behind her she looks a bit like the Japanese flag herself. Yet I get the feeling I better not say so. First she doesn't move. Then she snatches the flag off the refrigerator, so fast the magnets go flying. Two of them land on the stove. She crumples up the paper. She hisses at Sherman, "*This is the U.S. of A., do you hear me!*"

Sherman hears her.

"You call your mother right now, tell her come pick you up."

He understands perfectly. *I*, on the other hand, am stymied. How can two people who don't really speak English understand each other better than I can understand them? "But, Ma," I say.

"Don't *Ma* me," she says.

Later on she explains that World War II was in China, too. "Hitler," I say. "Nazis. Volkswagens." I know the

Japanese were on the wrong side, because they bombed Pearl Harbor. My mother explains about before that. The Napkin Massacre. "*Nan*-king," she corrects me.

"Are you sure?" I say. "In school, they said the war was about putting the Jews in ovens."

"Also about ovens."

"About both?"

"Both."

"That's not what they said in school."

"*Just forget about school.*"

Forget about school? "I thought we moved here for the schools."

"We moved here," she says, "for your education."

Sometimes I have no idea what she's talking about.

"I like Sherman," I say after a while.

"He's nice boy," she agrees.

Meaning what? I would ask, except that my dad's just come home, which means it's time to start talking about whether we should build a brick wall across the front of the lawn. Recently a car made it almost into our living room, which was so scary, the driver fainted and an ambulance had to come. "We should have discussion," my dad said after that. And so for about a week, every night we do.

"Are you just friends, or more than just friends?" Barbara Gugelstein is giving me the cross-ex.

"Maybe," I say.

"Come on," she says, "I told you *everything* about me and Andy."

I actually *am* trying to tell Barbara everything about Sherman, but everything turns out to be nothing. Meaning, I can't locate the conversation in what I have to say. Sherman and I go places, we talk, one time my mother threw him out of the house because of World War II.

"I think we're just friends," I say.

"You think or you're sure?"

Now that I do less of the talking at lunch, I notice more what other people talk about—cheerleading, who likes who, this place in White Plains to get earrings. On none of these topics am I an expert. Of course, I'm still friends with Barbara Gugelstein, but I notice Danielle Meyers has spun away to other groups.

Barbara's analysis goes this way: To be popular, you have to have big boobs, a note from your mother that lets you use her Lord and Taylor credit card, and a boyfriend. On the other hand, what's so wrong with being unpopular? "We'll get them in the end," she says. It's what her dad tells her. "Like they'll turn out too dumb to do their own investing, and then they'll get killed in fees and then they'll have to move to towns where the schools stink. And my dad should know," she winds up. "He's a broker."

"I guess," I say.

But the next thing I know, I have a true crush on Sherman Matsumoto. M*is*ter Judo, the guys call him now, with real respect; and the more they call him that, the more I don't care that he carries a notebook with a cat on it.

I sigh. "Sherman."

"I thought you were just friends," says Barbara Gugelstein.

"We were," I say mysteriously. This, I've noticed, is how Danielle Meyers talks; everything's secret, she only lets out so much, it's like she didn't grow up with everybody telling her she had to share.

And here's the funny thing: The more I intimate that Sherman and I are more than just friends, the more it seems we actually are. It's the old imagination giving reality a nudge. When I start to blush, he starts to blush; we reach a point where we can hardly talk at all.

"Well, there's first base with tongue, and first base without," I tell Barbara Gugelstein.

In fact, Sherman and I have brushed shoulders, which was equivalent to first base I was sure, maybe even second. I felt as though I'd turned into one huge shoulder; that's all I was, one huge shoulder. We not only didn't talk, we didn't breathe. But how can I tell Barbara Gugelstein that? So instead I say, "Well there's second base and second base."

Danielle Meyers is my friend again. She says, "I know exactly what you mean," just to make Barbara Gugelstein feel bad.

"Like *what* do I mean?" I say.

Danielle Meyers can't answer.

"You know what I think?" I tell Barbara the next day. "I think Danielle's giving us a line."

Barbara pulls thoughtfully on one of her pigtails.

If Sherman Matsumoto is never going to give me an ID to wear, he should at least get up the nerve to hold my hand. I don't think he sees this. I think of the story he told me about his parents, and in a synaptic firestorm realize we don't see the same things at all.

So one day, when we happen to brush shoulders again, I don't move away. He doesn't move away either. There we are. Like a pair of bleachers, pushed together but not quite matched up. After a while, I have to breathe, I can't help it. I breathe in such a way that our elbows start to touch too. We are in a crowd, waiting for a bus. I crane my neck to look at the sign that says where the bus is going; now our wrists are touching. Then it happens: He links his pinky around mine.

Is that holding hands? Later, in bed, I wonder all night. One finger, and not even the biggest one.

Sherman is leaving in a month. Already! I think, well, I suppose he will leave and we'll never even kiss. I guess that's all right. Just when I've resigned myself to it, though, we hold hands all five fingers. Once when we are at the bagel shop, then again in my parents' kitchen. Then, when we are at the playground, he kisses the back of my hand.

He does it again not too long after that, in White Plains.

I invest in a bottle of mouthwash.

Instead of moving on, though, he kisses the back of my hand again. And again. I try raising my hand, hoping he'll make the jump from my hand to my cheek. It's like trying to wheedle an inchworm out the window. You know, *This way, this way.*

All over the world, people have their own cultures. That's what we learned in social studies.

If we never kiss, I'm not going to take it personally.

It is the end of the school year. We've had parties. We've turned in our textbooks. Hooray! Outside the asphalt already steams if you spit on it. Sherman isn't leaving for another couple of days, though, and he comes to visit every morning, staying until the afternoon, when Callie comes home from her big-deal job as a bank teller. We drink Kool-Aid in the backyard and hold hands until they are sweaty and make smacking noises coming apart. He tells me how busy his parents are, getting ready for the move. His mother, particularly, is very tired. Mostly we are mournful.

The very last day we hold hands and do not let go. Our palms fill up with water like a blister. We do not care. We talk more than usual. How much airmail is to Japan, that kind of thing. Then suddenly he asks, will I marry him?

I'm only thirteen.

But when old? Sixteen?

If you come back to get me.

I come. Or you can come to Japan, be Japanese.

How can I be Japanese?

Like you become American. Switch.

He kisses me on the cheek, again and again and again.

His mother calls to say she's coming to get him. I cry. I tell him how I've saved every present he's ever given me—the ruler, the pencils, the bags from the bagels, all the flower petals. I even have the orange peels from the oranges.

All?

I put them in a jar.

I'd show him, except that we're not allowed to go upstairs to my room. Anyway, something about the orange peels seems to choke him up too. M*is*ter Judo, but I've gotten him in a soft spot. We are going together to the bathroom to get some toilet paper to wipe our eyes when poor tired Mrs. Matsumoto, driving a shiny new station wagon, skids up onto our lawn.

"Very sorry!"

We race outside.

"Very sorry!"

Mrs. Matsumoto is so short that about all we can see of her is a green cotton sun hat, with a big brim. It's tied on. The brim is trembling.

I hope my mom's not going to start yelling about World War II.

"Is all right, no trouble," she says, materializing on the steps behind me and Sherman. She's propped the screen door wide open; when I turn I see she's waving. "No trouble, no trouble!"

"No trouble, no trouble!" I echo, twirling a few times with relief.

Mrs. Matsumoto keeps apologizing; my mom keeps insisting she shouldn't feel bad, it was only some grass and a small tree. Crossing the lawn, she insists Mrs. Matsumoto get out of the car, even though it means trampling some lilies-of-the-valley. She insists that Mrs. Matsumoto come in for a cup of tea. Then she will not talk about anything unless Mrs. Matsumoto sits down, and unless she lets my mom prepare her a small snack. The coming in and the tea and the sitting down are settled pretty quickly, but they negotiate ferociously over the small snack, which Mrs. Matsumoto will not eat unless she can call Mr. Matsumoto. She makes the mistake of linking Mr. Matsumoto with a reparation of some sort, which my mom will not hear of.

"Please!"

"No no no no."

Back and forth it goes: "No no no no." "No no no no." "No no no no." What kind of conversation is that? I look at Sherman, who shrugs. Finally Mr. Matsumoto calls on his own, wondering where his wife is. He comes over in a taxi. He's a heavy-browed businessman, friendly but brisk—not at all a type you could imagine bowing to a lady with a taste for tie-on sunhats. My mom invites him in as if it's an idea she just this moment thought of. And would he maybe have some tea and a small snack?

Sherman and I sneak back outside for another farewell, by the side of the house, behind the forsythia bushes. We hold hands. He kisses me on the cheek again, and then—just when I think he's finally going to kiss me on the lips—he kisses me on the neck.

Is this first base?

He does it more. Up and down, up and down. First it tickles, and then it doesn't. He has his eyes closed. I close my eyes too. He's hugging me. Up and down. Then down.

He's at my collarbone.

Still at my collarbone. Now his hand's on my ribs. So much for first base. More ribs. The idea of second base would probably make me nervous if he weren't on his way back to Japan and if I really thought we were going to get there. As it is, though, I'm not in much danger of wrecking my life on the shoals of passion; his unmoving hand feels more like a growth than a boyfriend. He has his whole face pressed to my neck skin so I can't tell his mouth from his nose. I think he may be licking me.

From indoors, a burst of adult laughter. My eyelids flutter. I start to try and wiggle such that his hand will maybe budge upward.

Do I mean for my top blouse button to come accidentally undone?

He clenches his jaw, and when he opens his eyes, they're fixed on that button like it's a gnat that's been bothering him for far too long. He mutters in Japanese. If later in life he were to describe this as a pivotal moment in his youth, I would not be surprised. Holding the material as far from my body as possible, he buttons the button. Somehow we've landed up too close to the bushes.

What to tell Barbara Gugelstein? She says, "Tell me what were his last words. He must have said something last."

"I don't want to talk about it."

"Maybe he said, Good-bye?" she suggests. "Sayonara?" She means well.

"I don't want to talk about it."

"Aw, come on, I told you everything about . . . "

I say, "Because it's private, excuse me."

She stops, squints at me as though at a far-off face she's trying to make out. Then she nods and very lightly places her hand on my forearm.

The forsythia seemed to be stabbing us in the eyes. Sherman said, more or less, *You will need to study how to switch.*

And I said, *I think you should switch. The way you do everything is weird.*

And he said, *You just want to tell everything to your friends. You just want to have boyfriend to become popular.*

Then he flipped me. Two swift moves, and I went sprawling through the air, a flailing confusion of soft human parts such as had no idea where the ground was.

It is the fall, and I am in high school, and still he hasn't written, so finally I write him.

I still have all your gifts, I write. *I don't talk so much as I used to. Although I am not exactly a mouse either. I don't care about being popular anymore. I swear. Are you happy to be back in Japan? I know I ruined everything. I was just trying to be entertaining. I miss you with all my heart, and hope I didn't ruin everything.*

He writes back, *You will never be Japanese.*

I throw all the orange peels out that day. Some of them, it turns out, were moldy anyway. I tell my mother I want to move to Chinatown.

"Chinatown!" she says.

I don't know why I suggested it.

"What's the matter?" she says. "Still boy-crazy? That Sherman?"

"No."

"Too much homework?"

I don't answer.

"Forget about school."

Later she tells me if I don't like school, I don't have to go every day. Some days I can stay home.

"Stay home?" In Yonkers, Callie and I used to stay home all the time, but that was because the schools there were *waste of time.*

"No good for a girl be too smart anyway."

For a long time I think about Sherman. But after a while I don't think about him so much as I just keep seeing myself flipped onto the ground, lying there shocked as the Matsumotos get ready to leave. My head has hit a rock; my brain aches as though it's been shoved to some new place in my skull. Otherwise I am okay. I see the forsythia, all those whippy branches, and can't believe how many leaves there are on a bush—every one green and perky and durably itself. And past them, real sky. I try to remember about why the sky's blue, even though this one's gone the kind of indescribable grey you associate with the insides of old shoes. I smell grass. Probably I have grass stains all over my back. I hear my mother calling through the back door, "Mon-a! Everyone leaving now," and "Not coming to say good-bye?" I hear Mr. and Mrs. Matsumoto bowing as they leave—or at least I hear the embarrassment in my mother's voice as they bow. I hear their car start. I hear Mrs. Matsumoto directing Mr. Matsumoto how to back off the lawn so as not to rip any more of it up. I feel the back of my head for blood—just a little. I hear the chug-chug grow fainter and fainter, until it has faded into the whuzz-whuzz of all the other cars. I hear my mom singing, "*Mon*-a! *Mon*-a!" until my dad comes home. Doors open and shut. I see myself standing up, brushing myself off so I'll have less explaining to do if she comes out to look for me. Grass stains—just like I thought. I see myself walking around the house, going over to have a look at our churned-up yard. It looks pretty sad, two big brown tracks, right through the irises and the lilies of the valley, and that was a new dogwood we'd just planted. Lying there like that. I hear myself thinking about my father, having to go dig it up all over again. Adjusting. I think how we probably ought to put up that brick wall. And sure enough, when I go inside, no one's thinking about me, or that little bit of blood at the back of my head, or the grass stains. That's what they're talking about—that wall. Again. My mom doesn't think it'll do any good, but my dad thinks we should give it a try. Should we or shouldn't we? How high? How thick? What will the neighbors say? I plop myself down on a hard chair. And all I can think is, we are the complete only family that has to worry about this. If I could, I'd switch everything to be different. But since I can't, I might as well sit here at the table for a while, discussing what I know how to discuss. I nod and listen to the rest.

"What Means Switch" Discussion

1. The theme in this story is defined early. Look at the first paragraph and explain how the author brings up the sense of unbelonging that is at the heart of Mona's troubles.
2. How does Mona establish her popularity after her family moves to Scarsdale? Why does she do this?
3. Mona refers to her mother as "my mom." The expression should conjure up an American mother, yet the picture the reader gets is of a very traditional Chinese lady. How does the author put this picture of the mother in the reader's mind?
4. When Sherman first arrives in her class, Mona thinks he is Chinese. Why does Mona panic when she sees him, and what is the significance of her thinking he is Chinese?
5. What does the title, "What Means Switch," have to do with the story?
6. Why does Mona's mother get so angry when Sherman puts the Japanese flag on the refrigerator? Why is it significant that the father comes home right after that to discuss the front lawn?
7. While Mona's struggle to define herself is special, considering her interesting circumstances, much of her struggle is familiar to anyone who has made it through junior high school. What part of Mona's troubles do you identify with most?
8. Why do you suppose Sherman doesn't kiss Mona on the lips? Why does he flip her?
9. Why do you suppose Mona suggests moving to Chinatown?
10. Why do you suppose the author chooses to have the Matsumotos' car tear up the lawn in the scene where Sherman leaves?

Suggestion for Writing

This story is told from an unusual point of view. Consider this line: "In another ten years, there'll be so many Orientals we'll turn into Asians . . . . But for now, the mid-sixties, what with civil rights on TV, we're not so much accepted as embraced." The narrator reveals herself as an adult, but she is telling the story *as she experienced it then*, with all the confusion of the time. This technique is tricky, but it creates an interesting perspective.

Think of an event from your childhood and tell it in the present tense just as if you were living through it right now. As the narrator, give yourself the liberty of revealing yourself as an older person. For example: "In a few years I will consider my hair my best feature, but right now it is my curse, a kinky mess of interlocking curls, and I've taken to wearing baseball caps to hide it."

Coyote v. Acme

by Ian Frazier

(First appeared in The New Yorker*)*

Perhaps the secret of writing humor lies in combining elements that don't belong together. Who would have thought of providing an inept coyote with a personal-injury lawyer? A writer with the wit and wisdom of Ian Frazier, for one. This short, delightful fiction will remind you of your favorite "Roadrunner" cartoons and at the same time entertain you with a pointed satire on the lawyer-driven mechanism we call modern life.

About the Author

Photo Credit:
Le Deane Studio

IAN FRAZIER is a staff writer for *The New Yorker*. His inimitable prose has appeared there and in other magazines, including *The Atlantic Monthly* and *The New Republic*. Ian is a graduate of Harvard University, where he wrote for the *Harvard Lampoon*. His books, DATING YOUR MOM, NOBODY BETTER, BETTER THAN NOBODY, and GREAT PLAINS (Farrar, Straus & Giroux), have all been critically acclaimed.

IN THE UNITED STATES DISTRICT COURT,
SOUTHWESTERN DISTRICT, TEMPE, ARIZONA
CASE NO. B19294, JUDGE JOAN KUJAVA, PRESIDING
WILE E. COYOTE, PLAINTIFF
-V.-
ACME COMPANY, DEFENDANT

Opening Statement of Mr. Harold Schoff, attorney for Mr. Coyote: My client, Mr. Wile E. Coyote, a resident of Arizona and contiguous states, does hereby bring suit for damages against the Acme Company, manufacturer and retail distributor of assorted merchandise, incorporated in Delaware and doing business in every state, district, and territory. Mr. Coyote seeks compensation for personal injuries, loss of business income, and mental suffering caused as a direct result of the actions and/or gross negligence of said company, under Title 15 of the United States Code, Chapter 47, section 2072, subsection (a), relating to product liability.

Mr. Coyote states that on eighty-five separate occasions he has purchased of the Acme Company (hereinafter, "Defendant"), through that company's mail-order department, certain products which did cause him bodily injury due to defects in manufacture or improper cautionary labelling. Sales slips made out to Mr. Coyote as proof of purchase are at present in the possession of the Court, marked Exhibit A. Such injuries sustained by Mr. Coyote have temporarily restricted his ability to make a living in his profession of predator. Mr. Coyote is self-employed and thus not eligible for Workmen's Compensation.

Mr. Coyote states that on December 13th he received of Defendant via parcel post one Acme Rocket Sled. The intention of Mr. Coyote was to use the Rocket Sled to aid him in pursuit of his prey. Upon receipt of the Rocket Sled

Mr. Coyote removed it from its wooden shipping crate and, sighting his prey in the distance, activated the ignition. As Mr. Coyote gripped the handlebars, the Rocket Sled accelerated with such sudden and precipitate force as to stretch Mr. Coyote's forelimbs to a length of fifty feet. Subsequently, the rest of Mr. Coyote's body shot forward with a violent jolt, causing severe strain to his back and neck and placing him unexpectedly astride the Rocket Sled. Disappearing over the horizon at such speed as to leave a diminishing jet trail along its path, the Rocket Sled soon brought Mr. Coyote abreast of his prey. At that moment the animal he was pursuing veered sharply to the right. Mr. Coyote vigorously attempted to follow this maneuver but was unable to, due to poorly designed steering on the Rocket Sled and a faulty or nonexistent braking system. Shortly thereafter, the unchecked progress of the Rocket Sled brought it and Mr. Coyote into collision with the side of a mesa.

Paragraph One of the Report of Attending Physician (Exhibit B), prepared by Dr. Ernest Grosscup, M.D., D.O., details the multiple fractures, contusions, and tissue damage suffered by Mr. Coyote as a result of this collision. Repair of the injuries required a full bandage around the head (excluding the ears), a neck brace, and full or partial casts on all four legs.

Hampered by these injuries, Mr. Coyote was nevertheless obliged to support himself. With this in mind, he purchased of Defendant as an aid to mobility one pair of Acme Rocket Skates. When he attempted to use this product, however, he became involved in an accident remarkably similar to that which occurred with the Rocket Sled. Again, Defendant sold over the counter, without caveat, a product which attached powerful jet engines (in this case, two) to inadequate vehicles, with little or no provision for passenger safety.

Encumbered by his heavy casts, Mr. Coyote lost control of the Rocket Skates soon after strapping them on, and collided with a roadside billboard so violently as to leave a hole in the shape of his full silhouette.

Mr. Coyote states that on occasions too numerous to list in this document he has suffered mishaps with explosives purchased of Defendant: the Acme "Little Giant" Firecracker, the Acme Self-Guided Aerial Bomb, etc. (For a full listing, see the Acme Mail Order Explosives Catalogue and attached deposition, entered in evidence as Exhibit C.) Indeed, it is safe to say that not once has an explosive purchased of Defendant by Mr. Coyote performed in an expected manner. To cite just one example: At the expense of much time and personal effort, Mr. Coyote constructed around the outer rim of a butte a wooden trough beginning at the top of the butte and spiralling downward around it to some few feet above a black X painted on the desert floor. The trough was designed in such a way that a spherical explosive of the type sold by Defendant would roll easily and swiftly down to the point of detonation indicated by the X. Mr. Coyote placed a generous pile of birdseed directly on the X, and then, carrying the spherical Acme Bomb (Catalogue # 78–832), climbed to the top of the butte. Mr. Coyote's prey, seeing the birdseed, approached, and Mr. Coyote proceeded to light the fuse. In an instant, the fuse burned down to the stem, causing the bomb to detonate.

In addition to reducing all Mr. Coyote's careful preparations to naught, the premature detonation of Defendant's product resulted in the following disfigurements to Mr. Coyote:

1. Severe singeing of the hair on the head, neck, and muzzle.
2. Sooty discoloration.

3. Fracture of the left ear at the stem, causing the ear to dangle in the aftershock with a creaking noise.
4. Full or partial combustion of whiskers, producing kinking, frazzling, and ashy disintegration.
5. Radical widening of the eyes, due to brow and lid charring.

We come now to the Acme Spring-Powered Shoes. The remains of a pair of these purchased by Mr. Coyote on June 23rd are Plaintiff's Exhibit D. Selected fragments have been shipped to the metallurgical laboratories of the University of California at Santa Barbara for analysis, but to date no explanation has been found for this product's sudden and extreme malfunction. As advertised by Defendant, this product is simplicity itself: two wood-and-metal sandals, each attached to milled-steel springs of high tensile strength and compressed in a tightly coiled position by a cocking device with a lanyard release. Mr. Coyote believed that this product would enable him to pounce upon his prey in the initial moments of the chase, when swift reflexes are at a premium.

To increase the shoes' thrusting power still further, Mr. Coyote affixed them by their bottoms to the side of a large boulder. Adjacent to the boulder was a path which Mr. Coyote's prey was known to frequent. Mr. Coyote put his hind feet in the wood-and-metal sandals and crouched in readiness, his right forepaw holding firmly to the lanyard release. Within a short time Mr. Coyote's prey did indeed appear on the path coming toward him. Unsuspecting, the prey stopped near Mr. Coyote, well within range of the springs at full extension. Mr. Coyote gauged the distance with care and proceeded to pull the lanyard release.

At this point, Defendant's product should have thrust Mr. Coyote forward and away from the boulder. Instead, for reasons yet unknown, the Acme Spring-Powered Shoes thrust the boulder away from Mr. Coyote. As the intended prey looked on unharmed, Mr. Coyote hung suspended in air. Then the twin springs recoiled, bringing Mr. Coyote to a violent feet-first collision with the boulder, the full weight of his head and forequarters falling upon his lower extremities.

The force of this impact then caused the springs to rebound, whereupon Mr. Coyote was thrust skyward. A second recoil and collision followed. The boulder, meanwhile, which was roughly ovoid in shape, had begun to bounce down a hillside, the coiling and recoiling of the springs adding to its velocity. At each bounce, Mr. Coyote came into contact with the boulder, or the boulder came into contact with Mr. Coyote, or both came into contact with the ground. As the grade was a long one, this process continued for some time.

The sequence of collisions resulted in systemic physical damage to Mr. Coyote, viz., flattening of the cranium, sideways displacement of the tongue, reduction of length of legs and upper body, and compression of vertebrae from base of tail to head. Repetition of blows along a vertical axis produced a series of regular horizontal folds in Mr. Coyote's body tissues—a rare and painful condition which caused Mr. Coyote to expand upward and contract downward alternately as he walked, and to emit an off-key, accordionlike wheezing with every step. The distracting and embarrassing nature of this symptom has been a major impediment to Mr. Coyote's pursuit of a normal social life.

As the Court is no doubt aware, Defendant has a virtual monopoly of manufacture and sale of goods required by Mr. Coyote's work. It is our contention that Defendant has used its market advantage to the detriment of the consumer of such specialized products as itching powder, giant kites, Burmese tiger traps, anvils, and two-hundred-foot-long rubber bands. Much as he has come to mistrust Defendant's products, Mr. Coyote has no other domestic source of supply to which to turn. One can only wonder what our trading partners in Western Europe and Japan would make of such a situation, where a giant company is allowed to victimize the consumer in the most reckless and wrongful manner over and over again.

Mr. Coyote respectfully requests that the Court regard these larger economic implications and assess punitive damages in the amount of seventeen million dollars. In addition, Mr. Coyote seeks actual damages (missed meals, medical expenses, days lost from professional occupation) of one million dollars; general damages (mental suffering, injury to reputation) of twenty million dollars; and attorney's fees of seven hundred and fifty thousand dollars. Total damages: thirty-eight million seven hundred and fifty thousand dollars. By awarding Mr. Coyote the full amount, this Court will censure Defendant, its directors, officers, shareholders, successors, and assigns, in the only language they understand, and reaffirm the right of the individual predator to equal protection under the law.

"Coyote v. Acme" Discussion

1. Translate into plain English the following phrases from "Coyote v. Acme":

    a. " . . . certain products which did cause him bodily injury due to defects in manufacture or improper cautionary labelling."

    b. "In an instant, the fuse burned down to the stem, causing the bomb to detonate."

    c. "The sequence of collisions resulted in systemic physical damage to Mr. Coyote, viz., flattening of the cranium, sideways displacement of the tongue . . . ."

Why is plain English less funny than the courtroom vocabulary? How does the courtroom style (the whole story is the opening statement of Wile E. Coyote's lawyer) add to the humor and satire?

2. Wile E. Coyote is referred to over and over again as "Mr. Coyote," and his "profession" is described as "predator." On one level this description works as simple humor: it's funny to think of a cartoon coyote as a "Mr." with a profession. But this description works as satire, too. How?
3. While some of the humor here is obvious—the formal, legal descriptions of familiar scenes from the Roadrunner cartoons, for instance—some of it is far more subtle. Take the description of Wile E. Coyote's run-in with the Acme Rocket Skates: "When he attempted to use this product, however, he became involved in an accident remarkably similar to that which occurred with the Rocket Sled." Why does this sentence make you smile?
4. How does the author reinforce the sense that this is a "real" lawsuit?
5. The Roadrunner is not mentioned by name once, yet his presence is felt. How?
6. If this were a real lawsuit and you were the judge, how would you rule?

Suggestion for Writing

Satire is difficult to write, but see if you can get started by using Frazier's idea. Think of a fictional character or a current celebrity and pair him or her with a professional of some kind: a doctor, lawyer, promoter, agent; or someone even more unlikely, like a pilot, schoolteacher, novelist, hairdresser. What is the connection between them? What does this person have to say about the fictional character or celebrity? To whom is this person speaking (in "Coyote v. Acme" the lawyer is addressing the court) and why?

Two Fathers

by Charis W. Conn

(First appeared in The North American Review*)*

Here is a poignant story of a boy who receives the perfect gift from a most unexpected source. Through the boy's disbelief of this gift, and his father's nonchalance about it, the reader gets a gift, too: a shimmering portrait of a father and son.

About the Author

CHARIS W. CONN is an associate editor of *Harper's Magazine*. Her fiction has appeared in *New Letters*, *The North American Review*, and *Harper's*. Her novel, THROUGH THE GREEN FUSE, will be published soon by Pantheon. "Two Fathers" was her first published story, and it came to her through memories of her grandparents' house and her own father's tales of growing up there.

Still trembling, back from military school, a hint of slimness lurking beneath abused baby fat, Norman stands on the sunny Southern lawn, blinking. A head taller, his father stands beside him, rich-bellied, smoking a cigar, and smelling of the store—of Orange Crush and iodine and beer. He lifts his hand in a great gesture; an arc which takes in the sycamores, the twittering birds, the sun porch, and ends, triumphantly, at the space once empty beside the driveway. There, an apparition has been conjured from nowhere while Norman wept amidst soaked sheets and catcalls far off in Richmond: a gleaming white shack, the paint so shiny it seems still wet, with two windows and a little pitched roof with shingles that match the big house thirty feet away.

He cannot imagine what it is, though he senses that his father expects him to. It is a constant problem: his father gesturing, glancing, holding his cigar and his fat lips just so, and Norman failing to understand, to hop to, to jump to the appropriate conclusion. The year in military school was supposed to remedy this failure of his to grasp the world's rough indications and act on them.

In the sun, his father is pronouncing some incantation for which he should be grateful. Part of Norman's problem, he's been told, is that he does not listen. And talks too much.

"Boy," his father's profile regularly intones, each evening, from his cigar-scented, squeaking green leather chair. "Boy, you musta been inoculated with a phonograph needle."

So now he concentrates on listening, happy, after all, that it is Daddy's voice he is hearing rather than those steely strangers at the military school with their hard, up-country accents. He has never felt quite at home with the rolling, Southern drawl of his family; his stuttering, his inability to say what he means always renders his speech staccato, shrill, somewhat hysterical. He can never speak slowly enough to suit his family. And their lazy tongues, the outlandish time they take to say nothing usually fills him with an impatience so great he feels terrified and ashamed. But now, his own home bright and near again at last, he basks in his father's molasses delivery.

"Nomun," he says, looking at the sky, a plume of smoke escaping with the syllables. "You had a tough yea', we all know that. You made a helluva lotta mistakes, but at least you had to fix 'em up yo'self. Yo' mamma and me are proud of you—even if you didn't zactly *shine* up there in Richmond."

His father smiles at his own little joke and takes a fortifying puff.

"An' in spite of all the expense, Ah think it was wuth it. And NOW . . . "

He draws it out. Here it comes, thinks Norman. He cannot tell if it is good or bad, but this little building before him must have something to do with it.

"An' now, we think we understand yo' limitations a little bettuh. I ain't sayin' we gonna make it easy fo' you. Just sayin' we think we know what you CAN and CANNOT do."

Norman is beginning to sweat in his itchy homecoming suit. He is thinking of Celia making their lunch in the kitchen, with a cold Pepsi Cola waiting for him. Celia usually only comes mornings, but today, his father told him in the car, she waited special just to see him come home. "Without pay," his father said.

His ears return to his father's voice and he hears:

"Mr. Ferris up to school tells me you're pretty good in that wood working shop they got up there. Says you make a pretty good carpenter some day. Pay's not bad. It's good honest work for a white boy."

He gets it. At least he thinks he does. And the shack begins to shine like an enormous, angelic cloud set feather-light on the damp grass. He can work in it! Be alone in it! He cannot believe his father would allow him such a luxury. Last summer, when he tried to knock together some two-by-fours in the backyard, his father pulled up in the car, got out, gave him a long look, and said, "You smash yo' finguhs, I ain't takin' you to no hospital."

He doesn't hear any of the rest of his father's speech. His toes, caught like animals in the cruel traps of his polished shoes, inch him imperceptibly forward towards the small white door. It even has a keyhole! But he's certain there's no key. His room is the only one in the house without a latch because, his mother told him, "Daddy don't want you burnin' yo'self up in there. We don't want no trouble gettin' to you if we have to."

Finally, his back soaked, his eyes tearing from the sun, he finds himself following his father's bulging figure towards the shack. His father stands beside the door and says with a smile, "Now don't go wreckin' the place. It cost me a bundle," and departs, loping across the lawn and driveway, his legs unaccustomed to uneven ground and large spaces.

Norman stands before the door, real tears in his eyes. This thing, whatever it is, is his. There has been no mention made of Arnie, his older brother. But he can imagine that there will be fights over it. And the baby. Will his mother expect him to let the baby play here? He almost cannot bear to open the door, for fear it will contain—what? The local bully, ready to pounce on him? Or for fear that he has once again totally misunderstood his father, has made up the words about the wood shop and Mr. Ferris.

He opens the door a crack, not looking in. The smell of new wood and paint fills his body as if he were lying inside a gigantic flower whose overwhelming exotic scent was created just for him, matched exactly to his own physical chemistry. He glances back at the house. No one is watching him.

He opens the door and emits a high-pitched sound he hardly recognizes as his own.

The room is larger than he expected it to be, and immaculately white. Tables of heavy one-inch wood stand against each wall, seamlessly connecting to form a square U with the door at the open end. The walls on the right and left each hold a painted peg board stocked neatly with tools; beautiful gleaming metal and polished wood. On one table sits a flat type tray filled with screws and nails and bolts and nuts of every description. And on the furthest table lies a pile of sweet-smelling new lumber: two-by-twos, two-by-fours, planks and even dowels.

Without thinking, he finds that he has slammed the door behind him and now stands leaning against it, his feet wide apart. In the sealed, silent room, he can hear his heart. For an instant the thought flits through his mind that his father does not know what the shack contains; that it is some miracle that has duped his father into inadvertently setting him free.

He sits on the little bench before one of the tables. The air is stifling, intoxicatingly hot. His mind expands dreamily in the heat. In slow, deliberate motions he later cannot remember, he stands, removes his fountain pen from his breast pocket, and begins to meticulously trace the outlines of all the tools as they hang on the white peg board, carefully avoiding the holes. To keep it steady, he holds each tool firmly with one hand, longing to remove it from its hook, caress it, see what it will do, but restricting himself to his purpose. His lines are even and deep and blue-black, the sharp nib of the pen making a satisfying dent in the paint. When he is done, and has blown them dry, he can close his eyes, run his fingers over the lines he has made, and actually feel the delicate incision.

Without thinking, he walks to the back, lifts a blonde plank from the pile of new wood, carries it to the bench and lays it down. Without searching, his fingers find the hand saw and the heavy right angle. Bending his back and neck over the wood until it hurts, he carefully draws a blue-black line across the center of the plank. Again, that delicate sinking of the nib into the clean, virgin surface. He presses his knee to the wood and drags the blade across it, a hair's breadth to the right of the line he has drawn. When the wood clatters to the floor, he puts the spare piece back on the pile and sets his newly-cut square of wood on the table.

Hunched forward on the bench, his tongue between his lips, his eyebrows already full of sawdust, he measures out his message and scrapes the words into the wood, ever so lightly, with the tip of a tiny nail. With an infinite patience he has preserved for this moment, he hammers small nail holes along the lines he has scraped until the words KEEP OUT are emblazoned across the top of the plank. Below them, in lines of nail holes, a skull and crossbones glares fiercely.

Still in his sweat-soaked suit jacket, he takes the sign to the door and with the finality of a coffin maker, he beats the longest nail he can find through the plank and into the clean white of the newly painted wood.

"Two Fathers" Discussion

1. If you read only the first paragraph of this story, what would you know of Norman's life?
2. Through her use of "telling" detail, what does the author tell us about Norman's father?
3. How has Norman fallen short of his father's expectations?

4. How has Norman's father fallen short of the boy's expectations?
5. How does Norman feel about his family?
6. Why has Norman's father presented Norman with a workshop? What does this tell us about the father that we would not otherwise know from the story?
7. What is the significance of Norman's final act, nailing the sign to his workshop door?
8. What is the significance of the line "With an infinite patience he has preserved for this moment . . . "?
9. How might Norman's life change now that he has a workshop? Think of both positive and negative possibilities.
10. Why do you think the description of the inside of the workshop is so detailed and precise?

Suggestion for Writing

The point of view of this story is Third Person Limited, which means the story is in the third person ("he") yet filtered through the thoughts and experience of *one* character, in this case Norman. Try rewriting the story from the father's point of view. How does the story change?

Lies

by Ethan Canin

(Appeared in San Francisco Stories *and* Boston Globe Magazine; *collected in* Emperor of the Air*)*

"Lies" is the tale of a young man who takes a headlong plunge into the rest of his life. As you read this story, keep its title close by, and ask yourself: To whom is the narrator speaking? Why is he telling all this?

About the Author

ETHAN CANIN accomplished the near-impossible with his first book, *EMPEROR OF THE AIR*: he made the *New York Times* bestseller list with a story collection. "Lies" is one of the stories from that collection, a story he says he wrote in one night, twelve hours before it was due in a college writing class. Ethan's stories have been widely published in both commercial and literary magazines and have won numerous prizes and awards. He is back in California, which is where he grew up, after living in Boston to attend medical school. He likes basketball, fishing, and carpentry. His novel, *BLUE RIVER*, was recently published by Houghton Mifflin.

hat my father said was, "You pays your dime, you takes your choice," which, if you don't understand it, boils down to him saying one thing to me: Get out. He had a right to say it, though. I had it coming and he's not a man who says excuse me and pardon me. He's a man who tells the truth. Some guys my age are kids, but I'm eighteen and getting married and that's a big difference. It's a tough thing to get squeezed from your own house, but my father's done all right because he's tough. He runs a steam press in Roxbury. When the deodorant commercials come on the set he turns the TV off. That's the way he is. There's no second chance with him. Anyway, I'll do all right. Getting out of the house is what I wanted, so it's no hair off my head. You can't get everything you want. This summer two things I wanted were to get out of the house finally and to go up to Fountain Lake with Katy, and I got both. You don't have that happen to you very often, so I'm not doing so bad.

It's summer and I'm out of High. That's a relief. Some guys don't make it through, but they're the ones I was talking about—the kids. Part of the reason I made it is that my folks pushed me. Until I was too old to believe it my mother used to tell me the lie that anybody can be what you want to. "Anybody can rise up to be President of the United States," she used to say. Somewhere along the line you find out that's not true and that you're either fixed from the start or fixed by something you do without really thinking about it. I guess I was fixed by both. My mother, though, she doesn't give up. She got up twenty minutes early to make me provolone on rye for four years solid and cried when I was handed my diploma.

After graduation is when I got the job at Able's. Able's is the movie theater—a two-hundred-fifty-seat, one-aisle house on South Huntington. *Able's, where the service is friendly and the popcorn is fresh.* The bathrooms are cold-water-only though, and Mr. Able spends Monday mornings sewing the ripped seat upholstery himself because he won't let loose a few grand to re-cover the loges, which for some reason are coming apart faster than the standard seats. I don't know why that is. I sell maybe one-third loge tickets and that clientele doesn't carry penknives to go at the fabric with. The ones who carry knives are the ones who hang out in front. They wouldn't cut anybody but they might take the sidewall off your tire. They're the ones who stopped at tenth grade, when the law says the state doesn't care anymore. They hang out in front, drinking usually, only they almost never actually come in to see the movie.

I work inside, half the time selling tickets and the other half as the projectionist. It's not a bad job. I memorize most movies. But one thing about a movie theater is that it's always dark inside, even in the lobby because of the tinted glass. (You've seen that, the way the light explodes in when someone opens the exit door.) But when you work in the ticket booth you're looking outside to where it's bright daylight, and you're looking through the metal bars, and sometimes that makes you think. On a hot afternoon when I see the wives coming indoors for the matinee, I want to push their money back under the slot. I want to ask them what in the world are they doing that for, trading away the light and the space outside for a seat here.

The projectionist half of the job isn't so bad, even though most people don't even know what one is. They don't realize some clown is sitting up in the room where the projectors are and changing the reels when it's time. Actually, most of the time the guy's just smoking, which he's not supposed to do, or he has a girl in there, which is what I did sometimes with Katy. All there is to do is watch for the yellow dot that comes on in the corner of the screen when it's time to change the reel. When I see that yellow dot there's five seconds before I have to have the other projector running. It's not hard, and after you do it a while you develop a sense. You get good enough so you can walk out to the lobby, maybe have popcorn or a medium drink, then sit on the stairs for a while before you go back to the booth, perfectly timed to catch the yellow spot and get the next reel going.

Anyway, it's pretty easy. But once I was in the booth with Katy when she told me something that made me forget to change the reel. The movie stopped and the theater was dark, and then everybody starts to boo and I hear Mr. Able's voice right up next to the wall. "Get on the ball, Jack," he says, and I have the other projector on before he even has time to open the door. If he knew Katy was in there he'd have canned me. Later he tells me it's my last warning.

What Katy told me was that she loved me. Nobody ever told me they loved me before except my mother, which is obvious, and I remember it exactly because suddenly I knew how old I was and how old I was getting. After she said that, getting older wasn't what I wanted so much. It's the way you feel after you get your first job. I remember exactly what she said. She said, "I love you, Jack. I thought about it and I know what I mean. I'm in love with you."

At the time the thing to do was kiss her, which I did. I wanted to tell her that I loved her too, but I couldn't say it. I don't mind lying, but not about that. Anyway, we're up there in the booth together, and it's while we have our tongues in each other's mouths that the reel runs out.

The first time I met Katy was at the theater. She's a pretty girl, all eyes, hair that's not quite blonde. It falls a certain way. It was the thing I noticed first, the way it sat there on her shoulders. But it more than just sat; it touched her shoulders like a pair of hands, went in around the collar of her shirt and touched her neck. She was three rows in front. I wasn't working at the theater yet. It was end of senior year and I was sitting in two seats and had a box of popcorn in my lap. My friend LeFranc was next to me. We both saw Katy when she came in. LeFranc lit a match. "Put me out," he said, "before we all burn." LeFranc plays trumpet. He doesn't know what to say to a girl.

During the bright parts of the movie I keep looking at her neck. She's with three other girls we don't recognize. It turns out they go to Catholic school, which is why we don't know them. Then about halfway through she gets up by herself and heads back up the aisle. LeFranc breathes out and lights another match. I smile and think about following her back to the candy counter, where I might say something, but there's always the chance that she's gone out to the ladies' room instead and then where would I be? Time is on my side, so I decide to wait. The movie is *The Right Stuff*. They're taking up the supersonic planes when this is happening. They're talking about the envelope, and I don't know what that means, and then suddenly Katy's sitting next to me. I don't know where she came from. "Can I have some popcorn?" she says.

"You can have the whole box," I answer. I don't know where this comes from either, but it's the perfect thing to say and I feel a little bit of my life happening. On the other side LeFranc is still as an Indian. I push the bucket toward Katy. Her hands are milk.

She takes a few pieces and holds them with her palm flat up. Already I'm thinking, That's something I would never do—the way she holds the little popped kernels like that. Then she chews them slowly, one by one, while I pretend to watch the movie. Things come into my head.

After the movie I talk to her a little and so we go on a

few dates. In the meantime I get the theater job and in August she invites me to her sister's wedding. Her sister's marrying a guy twenty years older named Hank. It's at a big church in Saugus. By this time Katy and I've kissed maybe two hours total. She always bites a piece of Juicy Fruit in two when we're done and gives me half.

Anyway, at the wedding I walk in wearing a coat and tie and have to meet her parents. Her father's got something wrong with one of his eyes. I'm not sure which one's the bad one, and I'm worried he's thinking I'm shifty because I'm not sure which one to look at. We shake hands and he doesn't say anything. We put our hands down and he still doesn't say anything.

"I've been at work," I say. It's a line I've thought about.

"I don't know what the hell you kids want," he says then. That's exactly what he says. I look at him. I realize he's drunk or been drinking, and then in a second Katy's mother's all over him. At practically the same time she's also kissing me on the cheek and telling me I look good in my suit and pulling Katy over from where she's talking with a couple of her girlfriends.

For the ceremony we sit in the pews. I'm on the aisle, with her mother one row in front and a couple of seats over so that I can see all the pleats and hems and miniature flowers sewn into her dress. I can hear her breathing. The father, who's paid for the whole bagful, is pacing behind the nave door waiting to give away the bride. Katy's back there too, with the other maids. They're wearing these dresses that stay up without straps. The wedding starts and the maids come up the aisle finally, ahead of the bride, in those dresses that remind you all the time. Katy's at the front, and when they pass me, stepping slowly, she leans over and gives me half a piece of Juicy Fruit.

So anyway, we've already been to a wedding together and

maybe thanks to that I'm not so scared of our own, which is coming up. It's going to be in November. A fall wedding. Though actually it's not going to be a wedding at all but just something done by a justice of the peace. It's better that way. I had enough the first time, seeing Katy's father pace. He had loose skin on his face and a tired look and I don't want that at our wedding.

And besides, things are changing. I'm not sure who I'd want to come to a big wedding. I'm eighteen in two months and so is Katy, and to tell the truth I'm starting to get tired of my friends. It's another phase I'm coming into, probably. My friends are Hadley and Mike and LeFranc. LeFranc is my best friend. Katy doesn't like Hadley or Mike and she thinks LeFranc is okay mostly because he was there when we met. But LeFranc plays amazing trumpet, and if there's a way for him to play at the justice-of-the peace wedding I'm going to get him to do it. I want him to play because sometimes I think about how this bit with Katy started and how fast it's gone, and it kind of stuns me that this is what happened, that of all the ways a life can turn out this is the way mine is going to.

We didn't get up to Fountain Lake until a couple of months after her sister's wedding. It's a Sunday and I'm sitting on the red-and-black carpet of Able's lobby steps eating a medium popcorn and waiting for the reel change to come. Able himself is upstairs in the office, so I'm just sitting there, watching the sun outside through the ticket window, thinking this is the kind of day I'd rather be doing something else. The clowns out front have their shirts off. They're hanging around out there and I'm sitting in the lobby when a car honks and then honks again. I look over and I'm so surprised I think the sun's doing something to my eyes. It's Katy in a red Cadillac. It's got whitewalls and chrome and she's honking at me. I don't even know where she learned to drive. But she honks again and the guys out front start to laugh and point inside the theater. What's funny is that I know they can't see inside because of the tint, but they're pointing right at me anyway.

There's certain times in your life when you do things and then have to stick to them later, and nobody likes to do that. But this was one of them, and Katy was going to honk again if I didn't do something. My father has a saying about it being like getting caught between two rocks, but if you knew Mr. Able and you knew Katy, you'd know it wasn't really like two rocks. It was more like one rock, and then Katy sitting in a Cadillac. So I get up and set the popcorn down on the snack bar, then walk over and look through the door. I stand there maybe half a minute. All the while I'm counting off the time in my head until I've got to be back in to change the reel. I think of my father. He's worked every day of his life. I think of Mr. Able, sewing on the loge upholstery with fishing line. They're banking on me, and I know it, and I start to feel kind of bad, but outside there's Katy in a red Fleetwood. "King of the Cadillac line," I say to myself. It's a blazing afternoon, and as soon as I open the door and step outside I know I'm not coming back.

On the street the sun's thrashing around off the fenders and the white shirts, and it's like walking into a wall. But I cross the street without really knowing what I'm doing and get into the car on the driver's side. All the time I'm crossing the street I know everybody's looking, but nobody says anything. When I get into the car I slip the seat back a little.

"How'd you get this?"

"It's Hank's," she says. "It's new. Where should we go?"

I don't know what she's doing with Hank's car, but my foot's pushing up and down on the gas and the clowns out front are looking, so I have to do something and I say, "The lake, let's go up to Fountain Lake." I put it in drive and the tires squeal a second before we're gone.

The windows are up and I swear the car's so quiet I'm not sure there's an engine. I push the gas and don't hear anything but just feel the leather seats pushing up under our backs. The leather's cool and has this buttered look. The windshield is tinted at the top. After about three blocks I start thinking to myself, I'm out, and I wheel the Cadillac out Jamaicaway toward the river. I really don't know the way up to Fountain Lake. Katy doesn't either, though, so I don't ask her.

We cross over the river at BU and head up Memorial Drive, past all the college students on the lawns throwing Frisbees and plastic footballs. Over by Harvard they're pulling rowing sculls out of the water. They're all wearing their red jackets and holding big glasses of beer while they work. The grass is so green it hurts my eyes.

On the long stretch past Boylston I put down the electric window and hold my arm out so that the air picks it up like a wing when we speed up, and then, just before we get out to the highway, something clicks in my head and I know it's time to change the reel. I touch the brakes for a second. I count to five and imagine the theater going dark, then one of the wives in the audience saying something out loud, real irate. I see Mr. Able opening the door to the projection booth, the expression on his face just like one my father has. It's a certain look, half like he's hit somebody and half like somebody's hit him. But then as we come out onto Route 2 and I hit the gas hard one of my father's sayings comes to me, that it's all water over the bridge, and it's like inside my head another reel suddenly runs out. Just like that, that part of my life is gone.

By the time we're out past Lincoln I'm really not thinking anything except Wow, we're out of here. The car feels good. You get a feeling sometimes right after you do something.

Katy's next to me with her real tight body and the soft way girls look, and I'm no kid anymore. I think about how nice it would be to be able to take the car whenever you want and go up to the lake. I'm thinking all this and floating the car around big wide turns, and I can see the hills now way up the road in front of us. I look over at Katy, and then at the long yellow line sliding under the front of the car, and it seems to me that I'm doing something big. All the time Katy's just sitting there. Then she says, "I can't believe it."

She's right. I'm on the way to Fountain Lake, going fast in a car, the red arrow shivering around seventy-five in the dial, a girl next to me, pretty, smelling the nice way girls do. And I turn to her and I don't know why except you get a feeling when you finally bust out, and I say, "I love you, Katy," in a certain kind of voice, my foot crushing the accelerator and the car booming along the straightaways like it's some kind of rocket.

"Lies" Discussion

1. Why do you suppose Jack, who is barely eighteen, is going to get married?
2. Katy says she has thought about it and "knows" she's in love with Jack. Do you believe this?
3. Jack opens his story with a strong, subtle portrait of his father. In what way is Jack like his father?
4. In what ways are Jack and his father different?
5. Jack seems to think he's "not doing so bad." What do you think? What are his prospects?
6. Jack feels he has outgrown his friends, that they're still "kids" and he isn't. Is he right?

7. Jack comes alive to us through his observations about his life, his family, Katy, his job, his future. How do you view Jack?

   Give examples from the story to support your view.

8. After he takes off in the Cadillac, Jack realizes he doesn't know the way to Fountain Lake. How is this realization a metaphor for his life?

9. As he comes out to Route 2 in the Cadillac, Jack observes: "Just like that, that part of my life is gone." What does he mean?

10. What does the title of this story mean to you?

Suggestion for Writing

Have you ever made a choice you regretted, then stayed to take the consequences? Have you ever run from your choices? Write about an experience that involves choice and consequences, using yourself or an invented character as the narrator of your story.

Allison's Hair

by Monica Wood

(*First appeared in* The North American Review)

Allison is a 20-year-old woman whose life appears to have few turns left in it. Although she would rather ignore her young son than acknowledge him, he suddenly comes to her attention in an unexpected way. Notice how the dialogue in this story, though slight, tells us much about what is going on in Allison's world.

About the Author

MONICA WOOD is the editor of this book. Her short stories have appeared in numerous magazines and anthologies, including *Redbook*, *Yankee*, *The North American Review*, *Fiction Network*, and SUDDEN FICTION INTERNATIONAL. Her story "Wish" was featured on American Public Radio as part of the series *Readings for the Season* in 1989 and 1990. Monica is a former teacher and counselor who still does an occasional stint as a singer. She lives in Portland, Maine, with her husband and two cats.

Being pregnant ruined Allison's hair. It used to be very blonde, naturally wavy, and full of highlights. Now it is limp and the color of shredded wheat. She stares at it in the mirror, trying to perk it up with some combs her mother bought at the hairdresser. Nothing works. She looks at her face, the unlovely hair, the blotchiness of her complexion. She looks down at her body, naked and white, flabby in the middle, and says aloud: "I am twenty."

Jonathan is a slow child. He was slow to roll over, slow to crawl, and even now is unsteady on his feet. He totters into her mirror view, carrying the yellow truck and Kermit the Frog that he is rarely without. His nose is runny, his mouth and cheeks smudged with jam. She turns her back to the mirror to really see him.

"Mummy hot," he says. Jonathan is four, and these are his only words, learned when he was two, when eighteen-year-old Allison refused to hold him all summer. "Mummy hot," she told him, "go play in your pool." He had obediently retreated to the blow-up wading pool, saying "Mummy hot" to the yellow truck and Kermit. Allison had not told anyone about his first words.

Jonathan looks like a homely little girl. His face is flat and pale, his mouth thin and red. He is towheaded; Allison has never cut his hair. It falls in fine curls over the sides of his face, over the soft indentations left by forceps. He is dressed in a striped shirt with matching shorts, and slippers with cats on them. When Jonathan stares at her nakedness, Allison gets up to put on a robe. "Hi, Jonathan," she says, touches his head, and leaves the room. Jonathan toddles over to her bureau and uncorks her perfume bottle. He pours it over his shirt and leaves the stopper on the floor.

In the kitchen Allison pours her own coffee. "I'm not helpless," she says to her mother.

"There's my baby," Allison's mother says, seeing Jonathan at the door. His eyes are small and close-set, red-rimmed. He has many allergies. "Whew! What have you been into?"

Allison knows that Jonathan has taken her perfume and dumped it on himself. She knows her mother knows. They have both stood at the door in silence, watching him, many times. Allison's mother thinks this ritual means something.

Allison gets up from the table and takes Jonathan by the shoulders. There is no expression in her eyes. "Stay out of my perfume, Jonathan," she says quietly. "Do you hear me this time?"

Allison's mother says nothing. She loads the dishwasher and moves toward the basement door. "Do you have enough clean uniforms, honey?" she asks. "I'll need one for tomorrow," Allison says. Allison's mother and Jonathan descend the steps together.

Allison works at Henry's diner, three T-stops from home. She enjoys the clatter, the smell of grease, the old fixtures, the talk. It was Henry who convinced her to finish high school at night. She is a good waitress: quick, friendly to customers, neat and clean. At Henry's Allison acts the way she did before she got pregnant.

Henry's is not popular with young people, but yesterday two of Allison's friends from high school came in for coffee. They were on a break from classes at Northeastern.

"Your mother saw my mother at Jordan Marsh and said you'd been here two years. I couldn't believe it was that long since I'd seen you," Holly said.

"I heard you got your diploma," Jean said.

"Night school," Allison answered, rubbing the counter with a wet cloth. She could have attended school right through the pregnancy—lots of girls did. She hadn't wanted anyone to see her fat belly. She spent the entire eight months and one week in her mother's house.

"How's Jonathan?"

"Fine."

They ordered two muffins and left a five dollar tip. Allison was angry.

"They think I'm some kind of welfare mother," she said to Henry in the kitchen.

"They don't know nothing," Henry told her.

Allison stays at Henry's because it makes her feel as if her life is on hold, waiting for something to happen. Restaurant work is temporary. It is what artists and actors do in New York, between shows. It is something college kids do when they are full of plans. She is working at Henry's "for now," she has told her mother repeatedly during the past year.

Allison regrets that Henry gave her the day off for her birthday. She thinks she has outgrown birthdays. She is an adult who pays room and board to her mother, who is at this moment suggesting ways to get Allison out of the house so she can bake a cake in secret. "Take him for a walk, Allison. You see him so seldom."

It is hot in the park, and Allison feels sticky and irritable. Seeing Holly and Jean yesterday made her ugly, and she has been thinking of them ever since. Jonathan sits on the bench next to her, watching her with his rheumy eyes. Goldenrod. Or smog. Or milk. "Here," she says, unpleasantly, taking his ball from his hands and throwing it a short distance. He goes after it silently, a little skip to his step, and falls over when he nears it. She sighs heavily, trudges over to him. "You're all right," she says, and returns to the bench, Jonathan trailing behind.

Jonathan does not cry. Allison thinks he was born without emotions. She thinks they both went into a coma at the moment of his birth and have never recovered. She thinks her mother is waiting for a cure.

Sometimes she thinks if Jonathan had been a girl, she would have been all right. At the end of the pregnancy she had begun to imagine a baby girl, putting her in hair ribbons and pink dresses. She began to think of being a mother as fun. Then Jonathan came, the homely boy.

Jonathan's father lives in Colorado now. Sometimes he sends money. He is younger than Allison, and when he offered to marry her it was with such a pained expression she told him to leave her life, which he did. She is not sorry about that part of it. She expects nothing from him, having never loved him. The pain and complications of Jonathan's birth she remembers as punishment for all her bad choices.

Jonathan climbs into Allison's lap, digging his small shoes into her calves for leverage. "Stop that," she says, and lifts him to her. He will not get down. She carries him home, his face deep in her hair.

Allison's mother is decorating the cake, a spice cake with peanut butter frosting. The decorations are the same every year: pink candle holders with pink and white striped candles. The cake decorating chatter is also the same, except now she addresses Jonathan instead of Allison's father, long dead, or Allison herself. "On the day your Mummy was born," she tells him, "the mercury hit one hundred. The hospital had no air conditioning and I thought I'd pass out." Allison smiles out of pure habit. Jonathan sees her and shows his narrow teeth.

"Do you want to come with Grammy?" Allison's mother asks Jonathan. "Grammy has to get Mummy a present."

"Don't," Allison says.

Allison's mother looks angry for the first time in years.

"Life goes on," she says, and takes Jonathan's hand.

Allison is on the couch drinking a Tab when they return.

"Grammy and Jonathan have a surprise for Mummy," Allison's mother says from the door, and something in the voice makes Allison turn around. Her mother stands behind Jonathan, whose curls are gone. He looks like a little boy with a man's hairstyle. Allison has seen pictures of first haircuts, and this is what they look like. His hair is parted severely on the side, closely cropped around the ears. The haircut magnifies the shape of his head; he looks like a slow child.

Allison stands up and opens her mouth. Jonathan's own mouth turns from a tentative smile into a wavy line, and his tiny eyes become moist and shiny. Allison stares at him, begins to walk toward him. Her bones feel pliant and stringy, she feels blood swirling in her head. As she drops to her knees in front of him, something breaks in her body. "My hair! My hair!" she cries, her hands in fists at her sides. "My hair," Jonathan says, pressing himself to her breast.

"Allison's Hair" Discussion

1. This story is written in the present tense. How does this technique help us experience what Allison's life is like?
2. Allison became a mother at a young age. How does the story hint at the fact that Allison is still just a girl in many ways?
3. Why do you think Jonathan keeps pouring Allison's perfume on himself?
4. Why do you suppose Allison doesn't want her mother to get her a birthday present?
5. The language in this story is simple and direct. Why do you suppose the author has chosen this style?
6. Besides making her feel as if "her life is on hold, waiting for something to happen," why do you think Allison likes working at Henry's?

7. Look again at the small scene where Allison's mother tells Jonathan about when "your Mummy was born." What does this story seem to mean to the mother?
8. What do you think this story means to Allison, even though she "smiles out of pure habit"?
9. When Allison sees Jonathan's haircut, "something breaks in her body." What is happening to her?
10. At the end of the story, Allison's hands are in fists at her sides, yet Jonathan "presses himself to her breast." What do you think happens just after the story ends?

Suggestion for Writing

Try writing a scene in which the dialogue is terse yet significant. People often say the most when they say the least. Imagine, for example, two people meeting again after twenty years, or a son visiting his father in prison, or a girl trying to tell her boyfriend she no longer loves him. How do people talk to each other in painful or awkward situations?

Cutting Weight

by Ellyn Bache

(First appeared in Seventeen*)*

This is a story about survival. Adele, the narrator, presents a sensitive portrait of her family, especially her brother, as they all come to grips in their own awkward way with a profound and sorrowful change.

About the Author

ELLYN BACHE, a full-time writer and part-time fiction teacher, is the author of a novel, SAFE PASSAGE (Crown, 1988), and CULTURE CLASH, a non-fiction book about sponsoring Vietnamese refugees. She says "Cutting Weight" was inspired by her son Matt, who began his high-school wrestling career as a 95-pound freshman. Ellyn lives in Wilmington, North Carolina, with her husband and family.

Our father had moved out over Labor Day, but by November it still wasn't official and we all pretended he was coming back. Every night at six-thirty I picked up my twin brother, Eric, at wrestling practice while Mom supposedly cooked dinner and the two younger kids set the table. Then one night Mom came rushing out as I was leaving, yelling, "I'll come with you, Adele, I need a few things at the store." Every time she went grocery shopping she forgot half her list. She was a mess. Before Dad left, she never let me or Eric drive if she was in the car. "Move over," she'd say. "You've had your license two months, I've had mine twenty-five years." But that night she slipped into the passenger seat without a word.

At school, Eric, who was trying to cut weight before the season began, was waiting in the dark outside the gym, hugging himself into his jacket.

"It's sixty degrees," Mom said. "Not exactly Arctic weather. When you starve yourself long enough, your metabolism slows down so much you never get warm. It practically stops." She claimed to know these things from her years as a nurse before we were born. I turned up the heat until Eric stopped shivering.

I was no longer sure who was in worse shape—Mom or Eric. After Dad left and Mom went into her zombie mode, Eric decided to wrestle at 119. I'd been watching him for three years at the high school, so I understood that wrestlers liked to be as thin as possible, but this was ridiculous. Eric normally weighed 127, and even then he was skinny. That fall he was a stick.

He'd begun dieting in late October, eating only packaged foods with a calorie count on the label. Mom said twins like us were no more alike than any brother and sister, but Eric and I had always been pretty much the same—even-tempered and sensible. Then suddenly he was buying Lean Cuisines and cans of ravioli and macaroni and lining them up on the desk in his room—spaghetti with red labels, macaroni with yellow. "Just don't touch anything in here," he'd say menacingly.

One day Todd, who was ten, and Trudy, who was fourteen, were in the kitchen eating Spaghettios for lunch when Eric came in. He grabbed Todd by the collar and yelled, "You got those from my room, didn't you? *Didn't you?*"

Todd just sat there. "I didn't," he said.

"You better not."

"The Spaghettios came out of the pantry," I said to him. "I can't believe you're ready to break his nose over pasta." Eric let go. With Mom largely out of commission, I was the one who had to stay calm. It wasn't easy. Everyone knew we weren't really upset about spaghetti.

"We're stopping at the store," Mom said when Eric got into the car. "I'm running a little late with dinner."

Running was hardly the word. For three months Mom had been moving in slow motion. She acted like she'd gained all the weight Eric had lost—not on her body, because she was long and lanky, but inside her head, where it sat heavy, making her slow. Aside from forgetting food, she sometimes let the housework pile up until I washed the dishes and Trudy did the laundry.

At the supermarket Eric and I helped Mom find lettuce, cucumbers, and the low-calorie bread Eric ate. A man at the checkout stared as if Eric were a concentration camp survivor. Then we saw he was Ben Craig, Dad's insurance agent. The first thing he said was "Haven't seen Marshall around for months."

"He opened up a new office down in Wilmington," Mom replied. "He's been staying down there getting it going."

"Yes, I heard." He paused. "We've known each other a long time, Lorraine," he said. "If it's anything more than that, you can tell me."

Mom gave him one of her Anne Bancroft smiles, which I couldn't help but admire. She was slow lately, but the smile was a dazzler, aristocratic and withering. "Marshall'll be home for Thanksgiving, Ben," she said.

Back in the car, Eric cradled the grocery bag on his lap. "I was going to take that guy down with a single-leg," he told us, "but I was too hungry."

In spite of everything, Mom had been watching Eric wrestle ever since Dad left. This was a surprise because she'd objected to Eric's going out for the team when we were freshmen two years ago.

"I've watched them try to kill each other on TV," she'd said to Dad back then. "Don't ask me to watch my own son."

"It's nothing like professional wrestling," Dad insisted. "This is not the show, it's the sport." But Mom wouldn't budge.

I wasn't eager to see Eric wrestle myself, but I felt I ought to go to his first freshman match. Having made varsity because there was no other lightweight, Eric got to wrestle first. In his body-hugging singlet he looked like a long, white pipe cleaner. "Not all wrestlers are the short, stocky type," Dad whispered, but anyone could see Eric was the only skeleton on the team; it did not look promising. Just watching him sit there made the tips of my fingers go numb.

The other team was a nasty, scarred-up gang who'd been talked into staying in school to wrestle. They called themselves The Lethal Weapon and had a reputation for forming a betting pool before each meet, which went to the guy who pinned his opponent most quickly. Eric said they always made their bets in front of rival teams at the weigh-in, as if there were no question of losing or winning by decision, but only of getting a fast pin.

Eric's opponent was a guy who'd spent time in a drug program, for which his eligibility had been extended. He was more man than boy—a short, fierce-looking guy who wore a screw, not an earring, in his pierced left ear. As soon as the whistle blew, he shot toward Eric's leg and took him down before I knew what happened. Eric struggled to get up from his stomach, but he couldn't move. I remember sitting on my hands until they began to get numb. Eric's nose was mashed into the mat, and the hoodlum was using his ankle as a lever to turn him over.

Eric was squirming like a trapped animal. The other boy had him on his back. Right then The Lethal Weapon must have realized that if their man won quickly, they'd have to concede their betting pool after the first match, and it would take the fun out of the evening. So they began to root against their own lightweight, shouting advice instead to Eric.

"Bridge. Bridge!" they yelled. Though Eric later claimed he couldn't hear much with his headgear on, he suddenly did try to bridge—to arch his back and keep his shoulder blades off the floor. It didn't work. The referee slapped the mat and blew the whistle. Eric had gotten pinned in less than a minute. He went back to the bench with mat burns on his cheek and tears in his eyes.

Going home in the car, he said, "God, I'm such a sorry wrestler I've even got the other team rooting for me." It was meant as casual sarcasm, but his voice cracked.

"They think they can psych you out with that betting pool," Dad said. "But you've got to learn to make them beat you on the mats and not in the locker room."

"I guess," Eric replied.

To me it seemed he'd be better off quitting, especially if he had to face ex-druggies with screws in their ears every week. But Eric and Dad seemed to regard this as an issue between just the two of them, so I kept my mouth shut.

Of course the news made Mom even more set against wrestling. "I will not watch my son starve himself for a month," she said, "to writhe around on the floor with some muscle-bound hoodlum."

After that, Dad and I went to all the meets without her. Eric won only twice freshman year, but as a sophomore he had a winning season. Mom still wouldn't go. Then Dad left, and she'd been to every preseason scrimmage and early meet, even though Eric mostly lost. I put down the losses to his hunger strike.

Dad did come home for Thanksgiving. Mom had predicted it, but we kids were suspicious, what with his long absence. But he stuck to his story: As a mortgage banker, he'd been waiting years to expand. Now Wilmington was growing—a pretty coastal town, perfect for a branch office, three hours away by car, thirty minutes by plane. Why did he always miss the last flight home on Fridays? Because he worked so late—and worked on weekends, too.

Even Todd didn't believe this anymore. "Parents of four kids don't get divorced, do they?" he'd ask. And Trudy would reply, "Don't be a dink."

So at Thanksgiving we expected . . . what? That Dad wouldn't look us in the eye, that we'd feel the tension between our parents, something. But there was nothing. Mom looked her usual self, aristocratic with her hair pulled back, lean in the tailored skirt she wore to serve the turkey. She didn't flirt with Dad but wasn't sarcastic, either. Everyone admired the meal; Eric nibbled sparingly. On Friday we had leftovers, and Dad and Eric practiced takedowns in the yard. Nothing remarkable. Saturday Dad said Mom had cooked enough, he was taking us out for lunch. Eric's weight was good; he would cheat a little on his diet. Dad winked. Mom laughed. We were lulled into a false sense of normalcy.

It was as if Dad had given Eric permission to eat. Steak, vegetables, little round potatoes. Finally he sat back, smiling. But then Dad announced he was leaving that afternoon instead of the next day. It was a three-hour drive, after all; he had paperwork to do before Monday. Eric and I looked at each other, and each knew what the other was thinking: We'd been bought. Sunday we'd be home with Mom, and Dad would be sitting on the beach with his girlfriend.

Who was this woman? We weren't quite sure. We'd been to Wilmington only once, on Labor Day when Dad moved into his tiny apartment. We swam and met the two women in his office—Beth and Tina. It could have been either. Both women were younger than Mom, though not so pretty. Both had noticeable breasts.

After Dad left, as if to punish himself for thinking things were normal, Eric cut to 700 calories a day—mostly the cans of ravioli on his desk. Instead of eating, he read Mom's cookbooks, testing the sounds of ingredients on his tongue as if they could replace actual food: "Confetti pasta. Sounds good, doesn't it?" His face paled to the color of macaroni, but *The Joy of Cooking* lay open on the counter. For a guy who'd never cooked anything but scrambled eggs, it was bizarre. The holiday issue of *Southern Living* disappeared into his room, where he gazed at the pictures more diligently than he did *Playboy*.

"Did you ever make a souffle?" he asked Mom.

"Never."

"Mincemeat pie?"

"No."

"It's not normal, a wrestler reading recipes," I said. He rolled his eyes. Anyone who wrestled was macho. The more weight you cut, the more macho. Superman, completely in control. I felt deserted. When you're twins, you get the idea that there's somebody to sail along with no matter what happens, even if your father leaves. But there was Eric, drifting away. If he and Mom collapsed simultaneously—which seemed ever more likely—who'd run the house? Not Todd and Trudy. Me?

The next week Eric's nose started to bleed in the middle of a match. The referee blew the whistle so the coach could wipe Eric's face and the mat, but the bleeding wouldn't stop. After a discussion of making Eric forfeit, they finally let him go on. Blood ran down his lips, but he kept at it. My own mouth tasted of blood, and Eric's skin looked like wax. Then the other boy got the advantage and turned Eric over like a sack.

Mom didn't say a word until we got home. "You're anemic, Eric. That's why your nose bled. There is absolutely no rationale for dieting so strenuously that you become anemic."

"Oh, come off it, Mom," he said.

"Red meat," she told him, ignoring his rudeness. "I don't care if you don't eat another thing. But I'm going to cook red meat every night, and I expect you to eat it."

Eric didn't reply. Why should he? It wasn't as if she had the power to put food in his mouth. It wasn't as if she had power over any of us anymore.

"We won't put up the tree," she said the following week. "We'll wait for Dad to do that. But we can put out the rest of the things so the house will look festive." I was half surprised she really expected Dad to join us.

It was Saturday and Eric had an away meet, but the rest of us brought down the Christmas decorations from the attic. Usually the family sorted them together, but that day Mom began to go through the boxes herself. She examined each thing with terrible slowness. It was clear she didn't want help. She came to an oversize felt stocking with pockets for Christmas cards, which always hung in the den. She looked at it and replaced it in the box. Todd kept asking for a job. Finally Mom sent him outside to cut magnolia leaves for the mantel. Trudy called a friend. I flipped through the college brochures placed around the house. None of this felt normal.

"Don't ask," Eric said when he came in from his meet. "I got creamed. Pinned in the first period." His face was pasty white.

"We put up the Christmas decorations," I said to distract him. "It looks nice, don't you think?"

"What decorations?" I thought he was kidding, but when I looked around, the den didn't seem very Christmasy without its usual felt stocking. Maybe it was because we'd always put up the tree along with the other stuff, but suddenly the whole house looked austere, even with its candles and magnolia leaves. Mom didn't believe in glitzy silver garlands or plastic.

She was in the kitchen, not even aware Eric had come in—moving slowly, weighted down, not paying us any attention. In her black turtleneck and jeans, she could have been some stranger with long arms and bony wrists jutting from her sleeves. They say a woman can't be too rich or too thin, but I saw it wasn't true. Mom's body was as austere and ungenerous as the rooms. In Wilmington, Tina and Beth were softer.

Dad always called before dinner on Saturday. He said he worked all day but then started missing his family. We didn't believe this. We thought he phoned as a duty, before going out with his girlfriend. Upset as I was by the idea of what went on in Wilmington, sometimes I imagined Dad with his arm around Tina (or Beth, I was still not sure which), picturing them coolly, as if watching from a distance. Since there had been no official announcement, this seemed safe. But when evening came and the phone was silent, I wondered if we'd entered a new phase. The phone didn't ring. Mom kept reading. I couldn't stand it.

I walked over to the couch. Eric looked so exhausted that I decided not to wake him, but suddenly he shouted, "No!" and startled from sleep into a sitting position.

"What?" I asked.

"Oh—I thought I was still at the match," he said sleepily.

I sat down next to him and patted his hand. "Can I get you something to eat?"

Eric slung his arm around my shoulder. "Yeah, what's for dinner?"

I shrugged. All week Mom had been making hamburgers and steaks, and Eric had been politely eating some. But now she was reading her magazine, and no food had been taken from the freezer.

"After the season's over," he said to me, "I'm going to cook about three nights a week."

"Oh, sure, and I'm going to swim the English Channel." Even Todd was a better cook than Eric.

"I will," he said, squeezing my shoulder. "I'll cook unless I have an exam, and sometimes we'll go out."

By now Todd and Trudy were listening. Todd nodded as if he believed Eric would take over the care of the family and everything would be all right. Fat chance. I shook Eric's arm off and moved away.

"The first thing I'm going to make is a roast with mashed potatoes," he said, ignoring me. "And chocolate cake for dessert."

"You better do that on a weekend," said Trudy. "You won't have time to do it after school."

"I'll make it on a Sunday. A Sunday dinner."

They all nodded as if this were perfectly reasonable. They

acted as if this were about food and not about Dad. We all knew he wasn't going to call. "Sounds more like Christmas dinner," I said snidely.

"So?"

I was really getting angry. "Your Christmas dinner is right up there on your desk," I shouted. "You can have the Christmas dinner in the red can or the Christmas dinner in the yellow can. Only three hundred calories a hit."

"Adele, leave off," Trudy said.

"Dump it in a pan, turn the stove to high. About the limit of your culinary skills, too. Who do you think you're fooling?"

Mom came in from the kitchen. "What's the matter, Adele? Why are you yelling?"

"Me? Yelling?" I screamed. I was sick of being calm. Eric wasn't the twin I remembered, and Mom wasn't the mother. Why should I be calm for strangers?

Mom's eyes focused, but she was far away. She said, "Maybe we should send out for pizza."

After that I didn't care about either of them. Just didn't care. The next day Dad called and spoke only to Mom. Her face went completely blank. "He won't be home for Christmas," she said afterward. "In fact, we're thinking about a separation."

"A separation? I thought you were already having one," I said.

"Shut up, Adele," Eric said.

I just stared him down.

Two days later Eric got up weighing 125. He'd have to lose six pounds before the meet that night, fasting and running after school. I figured it served him right.

Mom looked on the verge of tears, watching Eric starve and still gain weight. But she was distracted over Dad and didn't mention Eric's anemia or suggest he take a snack for after the weigh-in. No last pathetic attempts at motherhood.

That evening in the gym we watched Eric warm up with penetration drills. He was so pale he looked like he'd have trouble staying conscious all evening, much less wrestling. I bought popcorn and ate it with the box close to my face. I felt a little guilty but chewed on. At least I could smell salt and butter instead of gym shoes and sweat.

Mom clenched her fists when the meet started, but I kept eating, I was ice. Eric came out for his match. I stuffed a whole handful of popcorn into my mouth and offered some to Trudy. Then I saw Eric's opponent: the guy who wore a screw in his ear. Tiny kernels stuck in my throat. I could hardly swallow.

Eric had wrestled the hoodlum only that once. Then the guy was in another weight class. But now there he was, his body a solid mass of muscle. There's no way, I thought. I put the popcorn on the floor.

Eric didn't pass out, and his nose didn't bleed. That was something. First period ended with Eric behind by two points, second period by five. At the beginning of the last period the hoodlum dropped Eric into a pinning combination. It would soon be over. Mom reached down and grabbed my hand. She was clinging to Trudy on the other side, and Trudy was holding onto Todd.

I didn't want to care. But it was as if they were depending on me, as if being twins were stronger than anything, as if I were the only one who could give Eric the strength he needed. I didn't think, I just started yelling: "Bridge, Eric, bridge!" Exactly the way The Lethal Weapon had yelled two years ago, only taunting wasn't on my mind. I could feel the fury gathering in Eric's chest, gathering in my own. He broke a hold, turned onto his stomach. Sweat, pallor, and concentration appeared equally on his face. A second later he was on his feet. He got the reversal, put the thug on his back.

The guy grinned, as if to say, That's what you think, pal. I'll get out of this yet. But Eric was working so hard he wasn't there at all; he was only a weight on the other guy's chest. This was less about wrestling than about survival—about a kind of strength that had nothing to do with what you ate. Mom's nails were digging into my palms. The hoodlum tried to arch his back, but he was pinned. The whistle blew to end it.

The referee held up Eric's hand in victory. Mom raised her own hand, still clutched into mine and Trudy's, and Trudy raised the hand she held with Todd. A chain. It lasted only a second, but Eric saw. He nodded up at us. And winked.

"Cutting Weight" Discussion

1. How does Adele feel about her brother? Are they closer than most brothers and sisters? How do we know?
2. Why do you suppose the mother begins to attend Eric's wrestling meets only after the father has left?
3. What does Adele mean, after the father comes home for Thanksgiving and gets Eric to cheat on his diet, when she says: "Eric and I looked at each other, and each knew what the other was thinking: We'd been bought."
4. After Eric's nosebleed, when the mother orders Eric to eat red meat, Adele observes: "It wasn't as if she had the power to put food in his mouth. It wasn't as if she had power over any of us anymore." Why is this true? What is happening in this family?
5. Food is a central metaphor in this story: Eric's weight loss, packets of color-coded food, and interest in cookbooks; the Thanksgiving dinner; Adele's eating popcorn at Eric's last meet; and so on. How does the fact that the events of the story revolve around food deepen the story's meaning and help us understand what is happening to this family?

6. Another central metaphor in "Cutting Weight" is wrestling. How do Adele's descriptions of Eric's struggles on the mat help us understand what this family is going through?
7. Why does Adele get angry with Eric when he tells everyone he'll be cooking for the family after wrestling is over?
8. "After that I didn't care about either of them," Adele tells us after losing her temper with Eric. Do you believe her? Why or why not?
9. Eric's final triumph—with Adele and her family lifting their linked hands in the air as the referee holds Eric's hand in victory—is a turning point for this family. Why is Eric's victory so important?
10. The narrator, Adele, is telling a story about Eric. He is her "main character." But Adele is a character in this story, too. What does she reveal about herself, either consciously or unconsciously, as she tells somebody else's story?

Suggestion for Writing

In a first-person narrative in which the narrator tells about somebody else, there are really two central characters: the narrator, and her or his subject. If the reader does not learn anything about the narrator along the way, then the narrator is unnecessary to the story and the story doesn't work.

Invent a narrator who is telling a story about someone else, and see if you can make the narrator as vivid and important as the "someone else" he or she is writing about. Let's say a narrator named Alex is telling a story about his friend Angela. Angela is having problems with her boyfriend. Why is Alex telling this story? How does he fit in? Is he in love with Angela himself? Is he having problems of his own that Angela's problems somehow relate to? Remember that a narrator doesn't tell a story without a *compelling* reason. In "Cutting Weight," Adele tells a story about Eric because she is intimately involved in everything Eric is going through; the story's events affect her just as much as they affect him.

Why I Like Laurel

by Ann Patchett

(First appeared in Seventeen*)*

In this unforgettable story about two black teenagers forever bound by an unspeakable horror, the author's touch is at once compassionate and cruel. As the root of Delia's fierce protection of her friend Laurel is revealed, so are many painful and universal questions about the nature of God, responsibility, and friendship.

About the Author

ANN PATCHETT was born in Los Angeles and grew up in rural Tennessee and later in Nashville. Aside from a two-week period when she was eight and wanted to be a nun, she has always wanted to be a writer. "Why I Like Laurel" is part of a collection of stories about a family in Carthage, Tennessee. Ann has published widely, in such magazines as *Seventeen*, *Epoch*, *The Iowa Review*, and *The Paris Review*. She is presently working on a novel.

Last Sunday in church the reverend read us the story of Lot and his wife, but it didn't set right with me. You want to believe that God is making His decisions based on what's fair, not waiting around to trip people up when they're not paying attention. Most of the time I can see the logic behind it. Sodom and Gomorrah? Let it burn, there was no good in keeping it. But Lot and his wife, those little girls, they were trying to live the word of God. How easy can that be? They listened when God said, Don't look back, but maybe someone called out to her, maybe they were begging to come along or just saying good-bye. And Lot's wife looked, like any of us would, to see what was behind her. I don't know a God that would turn such a woman to salt. It was a small mistake she made.

To die is a terrible thing, but once it's done, it's done. Think of Lot spending the rest of his life carrying this woman around, a statue as hard and white as a tooth. She must have been heavy. She must have needed protection from everything. He couldn't knock against her or leave her in the rain. Think of how he suffered every day, looking at the last thing she saw frozen on her face. She never spoke to him after that, never reached out and held his hand, but he kept her with him all the same, hoping that the God he knew might change His mind.

Some days it feels like I have two bodies to carry through this life, mine and my best friend Laurel's. She shuffles her feet so slowly that I have to drag her to any place we need to be in a hurry. When we get there she just sits around, staring out the window like she's in a dream. Laurel hasn't said a single word since that night she saw him down by the river. That was 1942, three years ago. Since then she hasn't said *water* or *thank you* or *hairbrush*. Not *yes* or *moon* or *Delia*, which is me.

When it all began, her folks were worried. They even took her to a white doctor in Nashville. She'd had a real bad cold in her chest, so at first they thought that she'd just lost her voice, lost like a thing you can find again. But days went on and on and even though she got better, she still wasn't making a sound. They started to think that maybe the cold had done something to her, but when that doctor went deep inside her he said it all looked fine to him, that it must be something else. She had always been a quiet child, but not altogether silent. They tried to find the thing that closed her up, and when they couldn't find it, they waited for it to pass. But it didn't. She just kept staring and shuffling and not saying a thing.

After a while, folks stopped worrying and they started getting annoyed. They didn't like the way she came into rooms so quiet, it scared everyone half to death, having her suddenly appear that way. They didn't like that look on her face, so broken and hollowed-out that it made you look away. They thought she was playing a game that she wouldn't let up on and pretty soon they forgot how much they'd all liked her before. Laurel was like a ghost that made them shiver in July, and when she brushed up against them they would say they could feel her walking on their grave. Before too long folks took to crossing the streets of our small town when they saw her coming their way. When all this started we were ten years old.

Today after school I left her in the sun to rest while I went back to get a book, and while I was gone some kids took to beating on her. They thought if they hit her hard enough and long enough she would cry out and then they would know for sure that everything had been a fake. By the time I get there her dress is torn in half and she's on the ground, her arms around her undershirt, taking it.

"You!" I scream at them. There are four there, big kids.

They are not even dirty or sweating for beating on something so small. One of them is holding her leg up in the air. My body is shaking. I feel like I could fly into them, tear them apart like heads of lettuce in my hands. The words that come up are from someplace deep, it is not my voice, it is not what I mean to say. "Murderers" I call them. "Murder! Murder!" They let her go and run from me, not because they can't beat me too, but because my voice tells them I know something about murder. It even scares Laurel, who pulls back from me as I try to stand her upright again.

"I didn't mean anything," I tell her. She will not look at me now. It is something that we understand, we don't talk about it. "I had to get them off of you. You would have said it too."

She shakes her head and then goes softly down to her hands and knees, looking for the button she has lost. When she finds it, blue and shiny in the dust, she touches her ear, then studies the blood on her fingers.

I crouch down beside her and look at the blood too. "Sometimes I get so lonely," I whisper in the hurt ear.

She nods, not at me, but at the button.

I take her to my house, where Mama is reading to her sister Nellie on the front porch. Nellie is leaning back in the porch swing, rocking herself back and forth with the tips of her toes. Nellie can read as well as anybody, I guess, but she likes for people to read to her. Mama told me that her husband used to read to her and she got used to the sound of another voice telling her stories. After he died, I guess she missed that as much as anything. I read to her myself, now and again.

"Mama," I say, and she puts down her book and looks at us. Aunt Nellie is off the porch and on her knees beside us before you could say Jack Sprat. She touches Laurel's ribs with the soft tips of her fingers, she goes up her arms and down her legs, feeling, looking for a deeper hurt than what we could see.

"Why is the world so mean to Laurel?" she asks. Nellie is the only adult I know who still takes a shine to Laurel. Her own mother does not look at her this way. "I think you're gonna be okay, sore and purple, but living. I imagine our Delia fished you out just in time." She looks at Laurel's face. "Yes, she did."

My mama hovers over us, picking twigs out of Laurel's hair. You can tell by her face that it pains her to see Laurel this way, but she doesn't say anything. Laurel makes her edgy now, she isn't the girl she knew before.

"You take her in and wash her up," Nellie tells me, "and I'll find her something to put on." She kisses Laurel's face, the part that is just starting to puff up. "Pretty girl," she says.

In the kitchen I wash out the cuts in Laurel's hands and hold a wet rag against the corner of her mouth. "What you don't want to say is fine with me," I tell her, "but you've got to learn to hit a body. I swear, I'm not always gonna be there to get you out. I'll try, but we're growing up now. What's gonna happen in a couple of years if I get married and move away from here? You've got to start looking out for yourself."

Tears come up in her eyes, and I put my arms around her. When I hold her this way I can feel how small she is, smaller than she looks even. The top of her head only comes to right about my chin, even though we are the same age. I rest my chin against the part of her hair. "So I don't go," I promise her, "I don't get married. Who was I going to marry anyhow?"

In May of 1942, before Laurel stopped talking, Nellie married a man named Hank Groundwater, who everybody here called Nellie's Boy. He had been taking a bus from Fort

Campbell, Kentucky, where he was stationed, to Birmingham, where he had grown up. The bus stopped for gasoline and to pick up passengers, even though there weren't any that day. When Hank Groundwater saw my Aunt Nellie across the street, he cashed in his ticket for what was left of the trip. They were married not three weeks later. Long before people knew him, they knew he was the man who had fallen for Nellie, and they'd say, Look, there's Nellie's Boy over there. He never minded it, since that was how he thought of himself too. All the girls in the town, no matter how old they were, looked at him like a kind of living miracle. This was a man who had come here for love, who lived in a town without kin where nothing was his own, all to love Nellie. He had beautiful, straight teeth, and when he smiled it was as if he couldn't keep those teeth to himself a minute more. I can see that smile as clearly as if he were walking towards me today.

When he married Nellie, Nellie's Boy married us all. Me, because I was her niece, and Laurel, because she was my best friend. There was no boundary to his love, no end to the people he was willing to take as his own. If Nellie loved us, that was good enough, and there were few people that Nellie did not pull to her. For us he made kites out of wrapping paper and sycamore wood he whittled into long, thin spines. He brought us packages of clove gum, and he taught us to fish like men.

"Girls always watching," he told us, driving the end of the rod into the soft shoals. "A girl will wait all day, worrying over a fish. When's he coming? When's he coming? She holds the rod up close to her, like this. You think that's gonna hurry a fish? If anything, he'll see you peering over the water and head back the other way. Girls take their line out, they make sure the bait's on tight, then try it all another way. Now a man . . . " He headed over to the grassy slope by the bank and stretched out on his back. He was as long as a day. "A man respects a fish. He knows he's coming around, just needs time."

We went over to him and lay down too, one on either side. "This isn't fishing," I said. "We're not working a lick."

"If it's too hard," Nellie's Boy told us, "you must be doing something wrong."

So we lay there, the three of us in the sun. Nellie's Boy told us what it was like to be in an army that didn't let you fight. He told us what it was like in Birmingham and how sad it made him to think of all the people in the world who would never have the chance to know Nellie at all.

Twice he sent word by a boy who lived near them that Laurel and I were to come to the woods at the edge of the river and look at the trees. I would run to her house fast as I could and call up at her window, then the two of us would head off towards the sound of water. We hollered for him to come out, but Nellie's Boy was nowhere. We thought he was hiding, waiting to jump out and scare us to death. We looked up in the tops of the trees, thinking that's where he'd be, and after a while Laurel said, "Delia, look what's there."

It was a black walnut tree, like the thousand others around it, but it was hung with oranges, six of them in all, tied on so neat you'd think they grew that way. I put her up on my shoulders to pull them down. I could smell them, like nothing else in the world, and I said, "Laurel, this is California."

The second time it was apples. The third time we got the note, we couldn't imagine. It was October and almost dark. We had been sewing maple leaves, red ones, into crowns. We had just finished them when we got word. We knew that he was waiting for us, that he would watch for us from somewhere in those trees. We thought we heard his laughing once, but never found him there. That day we were sure to have better luck, so we put the crowns on our heads and started out.

"Where you think you're going?" my mama asked us at the door.

"We got a message, we're going down by the river."

"It's too late, past supper. It'll still be there when you wake up." She turned away, to tell us that we were through going over it.

"But it won't be there then, there're squirrels, boys, who knows what'll happen by tomorrow. Besides, it isn't even dark out."

"I've got to think about Laurel," Mama said. "Her mama worries about her when she sleeps over here. What will she think, me letting you go out like this?"

Then Laurel said, "Right back." It was about all the conversation she could muster, but it did more good than my talking. We headed out towards the trees.

"What'll it be this time?" I asked her. It was cold, and people were lighting their first fires. The air was full of wood smoke and dried leaves.

"Pears maybe. I don't know. Pears."

I nodded my head, that sounded right to me, then Laurel stopped walking. I stopped too. She looked around to make sure there was no one who could be listening. "Sometimes, I dream that I'm Nellie," she said. She turned her face half away from me. "I dream that we're married." Suddenly she got all nervous. "You wouldn't tell? Would you? I mean, you swear?"

"Sure," I said. I didn't tell her I'd thought about it too. I started to tell her this once, a long time later, but it didn't seem right anymore.

We started rushing, trying to beat the darkness. We split up, like a game, to see who could find it first. It seemed like we looked for longer that night than usual, maybe not, but we were close to the edge of the trees that stopped at the steep slope of the riverbank when we heard the noise. At first I thought it was Nellie's Boy, that I'd finally found him. I looked for Laurel and caught sight of her not too far away, she came towards me real slow, there was a funny look on her face. "I hear something," she said.

We slipped down beside a tree and listened, I thought it would be him, but as it got closer I heard the voices of men, loud voices. It was nearly dark by then, and a light mist of rain had come up from nowhere, the way it does that time of year. I could hear the sound of branches snapping as they moved towards us, and though I could make out their voices, I couldn't make myself understand what they were saying. They were laughing in a way that made me cold. I could hear the small yelps of dogs and then I could smell the dogs and I knew that meant they could smell me too. I heard one of the men calling for a dog to get back. By then we could see a light in the trees, and all the time it's moving towards us and I know this is not danger like in a fun house, but something serious, something you know to run from, like a rabbit knows long before she sees the fox. Then I could see them, six or seven, white, big, a few with guns. They wore caps and work shirts, one of them had a couple of dead possum. One of them tripped over a root and fell and laughed and got up again. I saw their faces. Laurel grabbed my hand tight and I tried to think of something. I told her to go down because there was no place else to go. We started down the steep bank to the river. A path had been cut by all the kids who played down there and it went right to left, left to right, making a zigzag towards the water. We half ran, half slid. This wasn't what he had come for, it wasn't what we wanted.

I looked at Laurel, at the red crown of leaves in her hair. I forgot I was wearing one too. "It's going to find us," she said.

But I said no. "They can't see us down here, they can't smell us so close to the water." I didn't know if this was true, but I wanted it to be true so I said it again. We waited and pressed against the grassy wall of dirt, the sound of the river taking away the sound of the dogs. We held our breath for so long I knew they must have passed us. I took a step back and tried to see up the bank. I felt as good as naked in the light of the new moon.

Then Laurel looked to the river.

In my memory she says, *Never tell*, though I don't know for sure she said anything. I think it could have been in my head, what I believe she would have said, had she been able to. But I hear it so clearly, her last bit of voice saying *Never tell*. And then she had me by the shoulders and the neck, pushing my head so hard into her that I couldn't breathe or move or call out. She all but broke me, she held me so hard. Little Laurel, who I could carry on my shoulders, had pinned me to her like an Easter flower. She was looking at the river and I was looking at nothing, at her sweater. I knew that there was something she saw and I knew it was bad and I knew I would have to see it too, because it was there, because at the time I didn't understand how bad bad could be. But there was no getting away. It was raining pretty steady by then, but she didn't seem to mind it. What she saw held her tight as she held me. I imagine how we must have looked that night, standing on the banks of the Cumberland, two little girls hanging on so close that from a distance you'd only be able to make out one shape, one person instead of two.

I don't know how she made the decision to turn away, to move from her sight, but after a week, a month, a year, she started to move me up the path, where the smell of fire and dogs still clung to the trees like leaves. She kept her arm wrapped tightly around my head and I went up beside her, bent over and shuffling. I scratched her and kicked but she wouldn't let me go and even now when I know for sure what she saw, and sometimes in the middle of the night believe I saw him too, this is the truth: I saw nothing but Laurel.

Once we were inside the woods, Laurel dropped me. Her arm fell slack away from my neck and I fell into the leaves. She took a few more steps and then sat down, as if she had suddenly decided it was all too much for her. The first thing I thought was how small she was, it was like she was growing smaller by the second, like she was bound to disappear.

"What was back there? Why didn't you let me see?" I forgot about the men and the dogs. I would let them hear me. I would go back. "You tell me or I'm going. You can't stop me this time!" This was so true that it wasn't even worth saying.

I think now that Laurel had used, in those few minutes, all the strength she had coming to her for her lifetime. She didn't ask me to stay, she didn't even reach out and touch my ankle, she just sat there. It was cold and raining and I was yelling my head off, but she looked like she'd fallen asleep. She had stopped me good one time, and that was all she'd be able to do.

I headed back towards the river, but I hadn't gone very far before I knew I wasn't going to find anything, not what had scared her, not even the river, which would be swollen now, washing away everything on the banks. The rain came down on me so hard I could scarcely find enough air to breathe. My clothes were so heavy with water that they pulled at me, and I started to feel a deep chill from under my skin. I thought of Laurel and made my way back to her.

"Come on." I pulled her up from under her arms. "We have to go now." She didn't say a thing, she just looked down. We hadn't taken ten steps when I felt something slap my face. It was a banana, hanging from a birch tree. I put my hand up to take it, but even the thought of it made me feel sick and lonesome. I left it there and guided Laurel home.

Mama was waiting for us with towels.

"What was I thinking of, trusting you with enough good sense to come in out of the rain?" She was down on her knees, pulling off our clothes. When I looked over and saw Laurel's face, I had to look away. What she saw left its mark on her, made her hollowed-out.

"Look at this girl," my mama said to me. "What did you do to her? Her mama's going to have a fit if I give her back looking like this." Laurel stood naked in the hallway, shivering. Mama looked up close at her eyes and caught sight of what was there.

"Lord girl," she whispered, "where'd you go tonight?"

Like I said, Laurel was a quiet girl back before all this happened. What with the cold she had and both of us feeling poorly, folks didn't think about the fact that she hadn't said a word since we'd come home five days before. It was, in fact, the same day they found Nellie's Boy in Nashville that they suddenly remembered they'd heard nothing, not even a *please*, pass from her lips all this time.

What I know about Nellie's Boy is in pieces, what I overheard or heard a long time later, when it was all stretched out of shape by time and too much telling. Not a word of what I know came from Mama or Papa or Nellie herself. They were careful to keep us from the truth, to close the doors and send us away when they had to talk about it at all. Nellie's Boy didn't come home that night we went to the river, and when Nellie went around looking for him, folks started to say maybe they didn't know him so well after all, maybe she'd been wrong to marry a man she'd only known for a few weeks. Tongues started wagging all over town, folks saying he ran off and left her, that he had a wife in Elizabethtown and another in Wartrace. But Nellie never heard a word, she went up and down the streets, stopping at every door, asking the same questions over and over again, Where did you see him last? What direction was he going in?

Nellie, she wasn't young when they got married. She'd waited a long time for him to come, without ever having met him or knowing who he was, she had waited. And that day he came, she went to him like you do your best friend who's been gone away for years. No way could she be wrong about him, she knew it as fact. She knew if he'd left her, things were bad, desperate even.

By the time they found him in the river, he had floated nearly to Nashville. Of course, they had no idea who he was. It was five days he'd been in the water. But Nellie had sent word in every direction, and after a while it came back that they had found someone, a colored man, whose head set backwards on his neck. It was by her that they identified him, by a picture of her he carried that for some crazy reason hadn't gone to a million pieces in the water. They say that not even Nellie would have known him, that he was so soaked up he was the size of three men, but I think that's just talk. She never was allowed to see him and there was no boat that would bring his body home. So they buried him, strangers, right near the river where they found him. It wasn't too long after that that Nellie moved down that way.

Once I figured it all out, I decided never to tell. They would ask Laurel everything, and when she wouldn't talk, they would make her take them there and draw pictures. I even dreamed about those men in the woods, their dogs and their torches coming after us in the rain. Dead is dead, there's nothing you can do about that. When they asked me what happened that night, I told them the rain came up and we lost our way. I said it was dark, we saw nothing, not each other, not our hands in front of our faces. "It was the rain that took her voice away," I told them, "washed it out of her." They will not ask me about Nellie's Boy directly.

Sometimes I think it is easier for me because I have a responsibility now. I can't spend too much time thinking about Nellie's Boy when I am looking out for Laurel. But there are nights after I take her home that a loneliness comes over me so strong that I feel a pain, a real pain, inside my chest, and I have to stand still and wait for it to pass. Those nights I go back to Laurel's and ask her mother if I can sit with Laurel for a while. When I'm with her, I don't hear the voices of the men as often. I don't imagine if Nellie's Boy cried out. It seems less like he's gone.

"Wake up." I push at her. There is a small light on her nightstand. Laurel does not abide the darkness. She looks at me and scoots over in her twin bed. I crawl in beside her. There isn't a lot of time, soon her mother will ask me to leave or my mother will come calling for me, it's late.

"I know you can't tell me," I whisper, "I know I shouldn't ask, but do you wonder if maybe we hadn't liked the fruit, if we hadn't said we liked it so much . . . "

I thought that tonight I wanted to say it, but now I don't. I lean my face against her pillow and smell the comfort that is Laurel. She puts her hand on the back of my head and holds it there until a voice comes up from down the stairs, saying it's past time for me to go.

It could have been either way, it could have been me who turned around and saw him there. I imagine one day, years from now, Laurel will see a dress in a shop window or a nice-looking boy across the street, and she'll call out to me to wait up: "Delia!" For one second she will forget about Nellie's Boy and the words will come rushing back to her. For me, there will be everything that Lot was denied. God will see where He was wrong and I will be there, like she was there.

"Why I Like Laurel" Discussion

1. Why does Delia open her story by wondering about the biblical tale of Lot's wife? How does that story relate to the one she is about to tell us?
2. At the beginning of the story Delia observes: "I don't know a God that would turn such a woman to salt. It was a small mistake she made." As we read the story, we realize that Delia is thinking of Laurel, not Lot's wife. Do you think Laurel made a mistake? If so, what was it?
3. Why do you suppose "Nellie is the only adult . . . who still takes a shine to Laurel"?
4. Why do Delia and Laurel automatically hide when they see the men coming through the woods?
5. Laurel musters all her strength to prevent Delia from seeing the murdered Hank. Remembering again Lot's wife, how does Laurel's forcing Delia not to look back relate to the last paragraph of the story?
6. How does Delia feel about God? What is her hope?
7. Why do you think Hank Groundwater hung tropical fruits from black walnut trees for Laurel and Delia?
8. One of the grimmest ironies in this story is that Laurel and Delia meet their horrible moment while looking for one of Hank's gifts of hope. In light of what you know about the history of black people's struggle for equality, why do you suppose the author chose to have the girls find the bananas just after they face what has happened to Hank?

Suggestion for Writing

Notice how in this story, the events are revealed slowly. The murder, which is the event that influences everyone's behavior, is not disclosed at the beginning. For a while we don't understand why Laurel won't talk. We *assume* that she has been traumatized, but we don't know why. This structure makes for a compelling, suspenseful narrative.

Try to write a story backwards in this way. Think of a central event that has a witness: an accident, the birth of a child, a fire, or even something as simple as the look on somebody's face. How does this event affect the witness? Can you begin the story with the effects of the event and in this way lead up to the event itself?

Homework

by Peter Cameron

(*First appeared in* The New Yorker; *collected in* ONE WAY OR ANOTHER)

This is the story of a young man who is just beginning to question the meaning of his life. When Michael stops going to school, everyone assumes he is reacting to the death of his dog. Perhaps he is, but as Michael's story unfolds it becomes clear that there are other, subtler reasons for his withdrawal.

About the Author

Photo Credit: Elena Seibert

PETER CAMERON grew up in New Jersey and lives in New York. His stories have been widely published in such magazines as *The New Yorker*, *Mademoiselle*, *Grand Street*, and *Kenyon Review*, and in prize anthologies. He has published two books, *ONE WAY OR ANOTHER* (a story collection that includes "Homework"), and *LEAP YEAR*, a novel, both from Harper & Row.

My dog, Keds, was sitting outside of the A & P last Thursday when he got smashed by some kid pushing a shopping cart. At first we thought he just had a broken leg, but later we found out he was bleeding inside. Every time he opened his mouth, blood would seep out like dull red words in a bad silent dream.

Every night before my sister goes to her job she washes her hair in the kitchen sink with beer and mayonnaise and eggs. Sometimes I sit at the table and watch the mixture dribble down her white back. She boils a pot of water on the stove at the same time; when she is finished with her hair, she steams her face. She wants so badly to be beautiful.

I am trying to solve complicated algebraic problems I have set for myself. Since I started cutting school last Friday, the one thing I miss is homework. Find the value for *n*. Will it be a whole number? It is never a whole number. It is always a fraction.

"Will you get me a towel?" my sister asks. She turns her face toward me and clutches her hair to the top of her head. The sprayer hose slithers into its hole next to the faucet.

I hand her a dish towel. "No," she says. "A bath towel. Don't be stupid."

In the bathroom, my mother is watering her plants. She has arranged them in the tub and turned the shower on. She sits on the toilet lid and watches. It smells like outdoors in the bathroom.

I hand my sister the towel and watch her wrap it around her head. She takes the cover off the pot of boiling water and drops lemon slices in. Then she lowers her face into the steam.

This is the problem I have set for myself:

$$\frac{245(n + 17)}{34} = 396(n - 45)$$

$$n =$$

Wednesday, I stand outside the high-school gym doors. Inside students are lined up doing calisthenics. It's snowing, and prematurely dark, and I can watch without being seen.

"Well," my father says when I get home. He is standing in the garage testing the automatic door. Every time a plane flies overhead, the door opens or closes, so my father is trying to fix it. "Have you changed your mind about school?" he asks me.

I lock my bicycle to a pole. This infuriates my father, who doesn't believe in locking things up in his own house. He pretends not to notice. I wipe the thin stripes of snow off the fenders with my middle finger. It is hard to ride a bike in the snow. This afternoon on my way home from the high school I fell off, and lay in the snowy road with my bike on top of me. It felt warm.

"We're going to get another dog," my father says.

"It's not that," I say. I wish everyone would stop talking about dogs. I can't tell how sad I really am about Keds versus how sad I am in general. If I don't keep these things separate, I feel as if I'm betraying Keds.

"Then what is it?" my father says.

"It's nothing," I say.

My father nods. He is very good about bringing things up and then letting them drop. A lot gets dropped. He presses the button on the automatic control. The door slides down its oiled tracks and falls shut. It's dark in the garage. My father presses the button again and the door opens, and we both look outside at the snow falling in the driveway, as if in those few seconds the world might have changed.

My mother has forgotten to call me for dinner, and when I confront her with this she tells me that she did but that I was sleeping. She is loading the dishwasher. My sister is standing at the counter, listening, and separating eggs for her shampoo.

"What can I get you?" my mother asks. "Would you like a meat-loaf sandwich?"

"No," I say. I open the refrigerator and survey its illuminated contents. "Could I have some eggs?"

"O.K.," my mother says. She comes and stands beside me and puts her hand on top of mine on the door handle. There are no eggs in the refrigerator. "Oh," my mother says; then, "Julie?"

"What?" my sister asks.

"Did you take the last eggs?"

"I guess so," my sister says. "I don't know."

"Forget it," I say. "I won't have eggs."

"No," my mother says. "Julie doesn't need them in her shampoo. That's not what I bought them for."

"I do," my sister says. "It's a formula. It doesn't work without the eggs. I need the protein."

"I don't want eggs," I say. "I don't want anything." I go into my bedroom.

My mother comes in and stands looking out the window. The snow has turned to rain. "You're not the only one who is unhappy about this," she says.

"About what?" I say. I am sitting on my unmade bed. If I pick up my room, my mother will make my bed: that's the deal. I didn't pick up my room this morning.

"About Keds," she says. "I'm unhappy, too. But it doesn't stop me from going to school."

"You don't go to school," I say.

"You know what I mean," my mother says. She turns

around and looks at my room, and begins to pick things off the floor.

"Don't do that," I say. "Stop."

My mother drops the dirty clothes in an exaggerated gesture of defeat. She almost—almost—throws them on the floor. The way she holds her hands accentuates their emptiness. "If you're not going to go to school," she says, "the least you can do is clean your room."

In algebra word problems, a boat sails down a river while a jeep drives along the bank. Which will reach the capital first? If a plane flies at a certain speed from Boulder to Oklahoma City and then at a different speed from Oklahoma City to Detroit, how many cups of coffee can the stewardess serve, assuming she is unable to serve during the first and last ten minutes of each flight? How many times can a man ride the elevator to the top of the Empire State Building while his wife climbs the stairs, given that the woman travels one stair slower each flight? And if the man jumps up while the elevator is going down, which is moving—the man, the woman, the elevator, or the snow falling outside?

The next Monday I get up and make preparations for going to school. I can tell at the breakfast table that my mother is afraid to acknowledge them for fear it won't be true. I haven't gotten up before ten o'clock in a week. My mother makes me French toast. I sit at the table and write the note excusing me for my absence. I am eighteen, an adult, and thus able to excuse myself from school. This is what my note says:

Dear Mr. Kelly [my homeroom teacher]:

Please excuse my absence February 17–24. I was unhappy and did not feel able to attend school.

Sincerely,
Michael Pechetti

This is the exact format my mother used when she wrote my notes, only she always said, "Michael was home with a sore throat," or "Michael was home with a bad cold." The colds that prevented me from going to school were always bad colds.

My mother watches me write the note but doesn't ask to see it. I leave it on the kitchen table when I go to the bathroom, and when I come back to get it I know she has read it. She is washing the bowl she dipped the French toast into. Before, she would let Keds lick it clean. He liked eggs.

In Spanish class we are seeing a film on flamenco dancers. The screen wouldn't pull down, so it is being projected on the blackboard, which is green and cloudy with erased chalk. It looks a little like the women are sick, and dancing in Heaven. Suddenly the little phone on the wall buzzes.

Mrs. Smitts, the teacher, gets up to answer it, and then walks over to me. She puts her hand on my shoulder and leans her face close to mine. It is dark in the room. "Miguel," Mrs. Smitts whispers, "*tienes que ir a la oficina de* guidance."

"What?" I say.

She leans closer, and her hair blocks the dancers. Despite the clicking castanets and the roomful of students, there is something intimate about this moment. "*Tienes que ir a la oficina de* guidance," she repeats slowly. Then, "You must go to the guidance office. Now. *Vaya*."

My guidance counselor, Mrs. Dietrich, used to be a history teacher, but she couldn't take it anymore, so she was moved into guidance. On her immaculate desk is a calendar blotter with "LUNCH" written across the middle of every box, including Saturday and Sunday. The only other things on her desk are an empty photo cube and my letter to Mr. Kelly. I sit down, and she shows me the letter as if I haven't yet read it. I reread it.

"Did you write this?" she asks.

I nod affirmatively. I can tell Mrs. Dietrich is especially nervous about this interview. Our meetings are always charged with tension. At the last one, when I was selecting my second-semester courses, she started to laugh hysterically when I said I wanted to take Boys' Home Ec. Now every time I see her in the halls she stops me and asks how I'm doing in Boys' Home Ec. It's the only course of mine she remembers.

I hand the note back to her and say, "I wrote it this morning," as if this clarifies things.

"This morning?"

"At breakfast," I say.

"Do you think this is an acceptable excuse?" Mrs. Dietrich asks. "For missing more than a week of school?"

"I'm sure it isn't," I say.

"Then why did you write it?"

Because it is the truth, I start to say. It is. But somehow I know that saying this will make me more unhappy. It might make me cry. "I've been doing homework," I say.

"That's fine," Mrs. Dietrich says, "but it's not the point. The point is, to graduate you have to attend school for a hundred and eighty days, or have legitimate excuses for the days you've missed. That's the point. Do you want to graduate?"

"Yes," I say.

"Of course you do," Mrs. Dietrich says.

She crumples my note and tries to throw it into the wastepaper basket but misses. We both look for a second at the note lying on the floor, and then I get up and throw it away. The only other thing in her wastepaper basket is a banana peel. I can picture her eating a banana in her tiny office. This, too, makes me sad.

"Sit down," Mrs. Dietrich says.

I sit down.

"I understand your dog died. Do you want to talk about that?"

"No," I say.

"Is that what you're so unhappy about?" she says. "Or is it something else?"

I almost mention the banana peel in her wastebasket, but I don't. "No," I say. "It's just my dog."

Mrs. Dietrich thinks for a moment. I can tell she is embarrassed to be talking about a dead dog. She would be more comfortable if it were a parent or a sibling.

"I don't want to talk about it," I repeat.

She opens her desk drawer and takes out a pad of hall passes. She begins to write one out for me. She has beautiful handwriting. I think of her learning to write beautifully as a child and then growing up to be a guidance counselor, and this makes me unhappy.

"Mr. Neuman is willing to overlook this matter," she says. Mr. Neuman is the principal. "Of course, you will have to make up all the work you've missed. Can you do that?"

"Yes," I say.

Mrs. Dietrich tears the pass from the pad and hands it to me. Our hands touch. "You'll get over this," she says. "Believe me, you will."

My sister works until midnight at the Photo-Matica. It's a tiny booth in the middle of the A & P parking lot. People drive up and leave their film and come back the next day for the pictures. My sister wears a uniform that makes her look like a counterperson in a fast-food restaurant. Sometimes at night when I'm sick of being at home I walk downtown and sit in the booth with her.

There's a machine in the booth that looks like a printing press, only snapshots ride down a conveyor belt and fall into a bin and then disappear. The machine gives the illusion that your photographs are being developed on the spot. It's a fake. The same fifty photographs roll through over and over, and my sister says nobody notices, because everyone in town is taking the same pictures. She opens up the envelopes and looks at them.

Before I go into the booth, I buy cigarettes in the A & P. It is open twenty-four hours a day, and I love it late at night. It is big and bright and empty. The checkout girl sits on her counter swinging her legs. The Muzak plays "If Ever I Would Leave You." Before I buy the cigarettes, I walk up and down the aisles. Everything looks good to eat, and the things that aren't edible look good in their own way. The detergent aisle is colorful and clean-smelling.

My sister is listening to the radio and polishing her nails when I get to the booth. It is almost time to close.

"I hear you went to school today," she says.

"Yeah."

"How was it?" she asks. She looks at her fingernails, which are so long it's frightening.

"It was O.K.," I say. "We made chili dogs in Home Ec."

"So are you over it all?"

I look at the pictures riding down the conveyor belt. I know the order practically by heart: graduation, graduation, birthday, mountains, baby, baby, new car, bride, bride and groom, house . . . . "I guess so," I say.

"Good," says my sister. "It was getting to be a little much." She puts her tiny brush back in the bottle, capping it. She shows me her nails. They're an odd brown shade. "Cinnamon," she says. "It's an earth color." She looks out into the parking lot. A boy is collecting the abandoned shopping carts, forming a long silver train, which he noses back toward the store. I can tell he is singing by the way his mouth moves.

"That's where we found Keds," my sister says, pointing to the Salvation Army bin.

When I went out to buy cigarettes, Keds would follow me. I hung out down here at night before he died. I was unhappy then, too. That's what no one understands. I named him Keds because he was all white with big black feet and it looked as if he had high-top sneakers on. My mother wanted to name him Bootie. Bootie is a cat's name. It's a dumb name for a dog.

"It's a good thing you weren't here when we found him," my sister says. "You would have gone crazy."

I'm not really listening. It's all nonsense. I'm working on a new problem: Find the value for *n* such that *n* plus everything else in your life makes you feel all right. What would *n* equal? Solve for *n*.

"Homework" Discussion

1. Contemporary fiction often features characters like Michael, who feel alone in the world. Why do you think this is such a common theme?
2. Is Michael grieving over the loss of his dog? Is there any evidence that he acted this way before Keds died?
3. How does Michael indicate that he feels alienated from everyone around him?
4. Why is Michael so interested in solving algebra problems?
5. What does Michael mean when he says of his father, "He is very good about bringing things up and then letting them drop."
6. Because Michael notices little details about the world around him, his plight seems very real. Give some examples of his eye for detail. What do they tell us about him?
7. Why do you suppose Michael is so fascinated by the pictures in the photo booth?

8. Michael's story ends with a question: What would *n* equal? What does he mean, and how would you answer that question?

Suggestion for Writing

In this story, the loss of a dog is a *metaphor* for a more general kind of loss and loneliness. Can you think of other metaphors for loss? (Examples: leaves falling from a tree, a house blown away in a storm, a highway built over some farmland.) Think of a metaphor for something in your own life that troubles you, and write two or three descriptive paragraphs that evoke feelings of loss and loneliness.

3A. Essay

by Hugh Gallagher

(*First appeared in* Literary Cavalcade)

Anyone who has ever anguished over the "tell us about yourself" part of a college application will appreciate this hilarious satire by someone who has been there. Some multipage college applications seem to imply that unless you've climbed the Himalayas or worked in an orphanage you just aren't unique enough to go to the college of your choice. Hugh Gallagher seems to be saying, "They want special? I'll give them special!" He gives the reader something special, too: deadpan humor in a little story that lilts like a poem.

About the Author

HUGH GALLAGHER is a student at New York University in New York City. His "3A. Essay" first appeared in *Literary Cavalcade*, a journal of student writing published by Scholastic, Inc.

3

A. Essay

In order for the admissions staff of our college to get to know you, the applicant, better, we ask that you answer the following question: Are there any significant experiences you have had, or accomplishments you have realized, that have helped to define you as a person?

I am a dynamic figure, often seen scaling walls and crushing ice. I have been known to remodel train stations on my lunch breaks, making them more efficient in the area of heat retention. I translate ethnic slurs for Cuban refugees, I write award-winning operas, I manage time efficiently. Occasionally, I tread water for three days in a row.

I woo women with my sensuous and godlike trombone playing, I can pilot bicycles up severe inclines with unflagging speed, and I cook Thirty-Minute Brownies in twenty minutes. I am an expert in stucco, a veteran in love, and an outlaw in Peru.

Using only a hoe and a large glass of water, I once single-handedly defended a small village in the Amazon Basin from a horde of ferocious army ants. I play bluegrass cello, I was scouted by the Mets. I am the subject of numerous documentaries. When I'm bored, I build large suspension bridges in my yard. I enjoy urban hang gliding. On Wednesdays, after school, I repair electrical appliances free of charge.

I am an abstract artist, a concrete analyst, and a ruthless bookie. Critics worldwide swoon over my original line of corduroy evening wear. I don't perspire. I am a private citizen, yet I receive fan mail. I have been caller number nine and have won the weekend passes. Last summer I toured New Jersey with a traveling centrifugal-force demonstration. I bat .400. My deft floral arrangements have earned me fame in international botany circles. Children trust me.

I can hurl tennis rackets at small moving objects with deadly accuracy. I once read *Paradise Lost, Moby-Dick,* and *David Copperfield* in one day and still had time to refurbish an entire dining room that evening. I know the exact location of every food item in the supermarket. I have performed covert operations for the CIA. I sleep once a week; when I do sleep, I sleep in a chair. While on vacation in Canada, I successfully negotiated with a group of terrorists who had seized a small bakery. The laws of physics do not apply to me.

I balance, I weave, I dodge, I frolic, and my bills are all paid. On weekends, to let off steam, I participate in full-contact origami. Years ago I discovered the meaning of life but forgot to write it down. I have made extraordinary four-course meals using only a Mouli and a toaster oven. I breed prizewinning clams. I have won bullfights in San Juan, cliff-diving competitions in Sri Lanka, and spelling bees at the Kremlin. I have played Hamlet, I have performed open-heart surgery, and I have spoken with Elvis.

But I have not yet gone to college.

"3A. *Essay*" Discussion

1. This piece is a satire. What is the author poking fun at?
2. Who is the piece supposedly being written by? Read by? How does the presence of both a fictional writer and a fictional reader let the actual reader—us—in on a joke?
3. What is your favorite line in this piece?
4. Read a few lines out loud. Do you notice how the prose seems to rise and fall, as in a poem? How does the author accomplish this?
5. Why is the last line, "But I have not yet gone to college," a perfect ending for a satire on the college admission process?

6. What does the "3A" of the title refer to?

Suggestion for Writing

Write a few paragraphs about anything at all, and pay attention not so much to what you write as how you write it. Vary the sentence lengths. For instance, follow a short, declarative sentence with a compound sentence that begins with an adverbial or participial phrase. Put words together that sound good to you. Again, don't worry about the content—for this exercise, style is all that matters.

Leo

by Sharon Sheehe Stark

(*First appeared in* The Atlantic Monthly)

In this lyrical, dreamlike story, the narrator, Jeremiah, relates a memory from his childhood. This is a complicated, multilayered narrative about a child's first acquaintance with and eventual acceptance of death. Some of the poetic words and phrases may feel unfamiliar to you. Try to let these passages wash over you: invite yourself into Jeremiah's dream.

About the Author

Photo Credit: Jerry Bauer

SHARON SHEEHE STARK is the author of a collection of stories, *THE DEALER'S YARD*, and a novel, *A WRESTLING SEASON*, both from William Morrow. Her stories have been published twice in *THE BEST AMERICAN SHORT STORIES* annual anthology, and "Leo" received a "distinguished story" mention in the 1989 volume. Sharon says that "Leo," although fashioned from many parts—none of them autobiographical—grew out of an event that had haunted her for many years. In addition to writing and teaching, Sharon runs a little flea market in Kutztown, Pennsylvania.

I laid eyes on Leo Jacoby for the first time a second before he landed on my back, having launched himself from the locust tree that marked the property line between our two houses. Hey, I was somebody's son. When I got my wind back, I went sirening home to my mother.

We were new to Shepherd Hills. In less than a week we'd discovered that our furnace was cracked, that our driveway became a lake when it rained, that the Stuvers, across the street, expected us to keep our little wicket of ornamental fence painted (as our negligent predecessors had not). Motorists straying into the subdivision were forever getting snared in its endless loops and cul-de-sacs. Our doorbell kept ringing. "How do we get out of here?" they wanted to know, their voices poised between embarrassment and panic.

"Now we have everything," my mother said, the day Leo flattened me, "including a genuine neighborhood bully."

What was not genuine was her jocular tone. I was an only child, born when she was forty-three and my father fifty, both well past the age when they might feel equal to even minor occasions of harm. So as not to infect me too soon with their rich suspicions, their fully ripened terrors, they managed to project what was, at best, a kind of nervous-shading-to-hysterical turn of good humor. So she threw me in the tub, all the while singing a shrill rendition of *my* song. "Joy to the World," it was called—the one that begins, "Jeremiah was a bull frog," and ends, "Joy to the fishes in the deep blue sea. Joy to you and me." Humming along, my father scrubbed all traces of Leo off my back. Then they dressed me, not just in clean but in brand new. The ruse worked. That night I slept as if still swaddled in the tenderly feathered, familiar swag of our old life in town.

Leo was ten, maybe eleven. People said he was small for

his age (as was I, Jeremiah), though at the time he didn't seem so to me. His face was egglike and, except for what cunning could do to his mouth and eyes when he considered himself unobserved, even pious-looking.

His second assault was more serious, somehow, because it occurred not in some ambiguous border area but in the undisputed middle of my own back yard.

From an old chenille spread I'd fashioned a sort of tent, stretching it between two sentinel-like Scotch pines on either side of the space earmarked for my father's garden. I can still feel the March damp seeping through my jacket's heft as, lying on my back, I tried to heat the shelter with my own breath, lost the while in a maze of the impractical meditations, the answerless questions and reckless conjectures, I was given to then: How many pennies would be required to pave all the driveways of Shepherd Hills? What if someone offered me three wishes to yell "*Jesus cheats!*" in church? And—an awful one—what if I had to decide which parent to rescue from a burning house?

The immediate yield of such thinking was enough fear and guilt to paralyze my brain. Small wonder Leo was able to move right in. Before I knew it, he was deftly wrapping me up in the bedspread. Then he stuffed me, bundled, headfirst into one of our king-sized trash cans and sent me bumping down the long slope of our lawn. I came crashing to rest against a rock in the little stream that ran through the woods behind both our houses.

"You're pushing it, buster," my mother said, as if Leo were right there, in our kitchen. She turned to my father. "Ben," she said, and "Ben" was all she had to say. Although confrontations of any sort horrified this man, he went next door immediately: what wouldn't he do for his Jean?

My parents had not passed the two decades before I was born in idle anticipation of me. Those childless years were the forge of a true marriage, a union that was if not perfect, then certainly impenetrable from without. Not that they actively excluded me. On the contrary, they were attentive, generous, tender, interested. But they enacted these virtues in concert, always, and the ferocious protections accorded me formed a single bulwark between me and the world, a wall so thick with their mutuality—with consultation, confederacy, and habit—that it insulated me from them as well. A child needs to separate his parents from time to time, even as he prays they will never separate. He needs to take one or the other for his own, to make his own faction. But the minutes of our lives were stitched into one lovely fabric, which was my parents' marriage. And me? I lived not in the weft of that cloth but under the amplitude of its shelter, free to leave someday.

My father returned from the Jacobys' looking benevolent and very pleased with himself. "You couldn't ask for a nicer couple," he said. "Most agreeable." My father's hobby was believing in people. "They promised to speak to young Leo," he told Jean.

"Speak?" she said, her fingers working as if connected to her vocal chords. She was struggling to modulate her tone. "That boy is well on the road to Morganza—that says kick-in-the-britches time to me."

"Morganza?" I asked.

"Nothing you need know about," she said severely. "Hateful place, home for incorrigibles." She looked at my father. Then, as always, the very sight of her man tranquilized her. "Truth, Ben—is that so wrong of me?"

"Jean, you're a hard woman," he said, with such delight as to imply that *hard* was in the same class as *compassionate* or *beautiful*.

In the morning light her face was papery, scored with tiny lines. Surely the move to the suburbs was costing her. She'd loved our smallish city apartment, the suite of four rooms of precisely identical dimension, each lamp and candy dish lustered with time and attention, each intractably in its place. When they announced we were moving, the reason too breezily advanced was chrysanthemums. My father had joined the American Mum Society and wanted "the chance to produce a prizewinner."

"Your old pa's a putterer at heart," she said with her patented half-smile, as she wet her index finger, testing the big, shiplike electric iron. I can still see the wreath of sweet, starchy perfume that rose from my father's shirt with her first furious stroke, making her sneeze.

By the time we moved in, the trees of the neighborhood were large enough to promise moderate shade by decade's end. Arborvitae privacy fences were beginning to close off views, though between us and the Jacobys' stood only that spindly locust on a strip of grass dividing our two driveways.

Because their driveway was wider and drier than ours, it was more desirable as a bus stop. I was in second grade, Leo in sixth. The neighborhood was rampant with kids in those days; the boom was still on. A goodly bunch of us were always hunched against the chill, or sitting alone on piles of books, on the tarmac. Some names that come to me offhand: Patty and Scott Tyson, Melody Kolson, Drake Stuver, and Junie Jo Levi, who wore tie-down caps to keep Leo from dripping glue in her hair or pasting her copper curls with icy spring snowballs.

Once he faked a heart attack and, staggering, plowed her across the grass and into our driveway, which happened to be, on that particular day, in its high-water stage. Another time he grabbed the two of us by the scruff of the neck and banged us together. Junie Jew and Jeremiah Jerk, the human chalk erasers. The others laughed in a way I can only describe as a controlled release of something disgusting, the way polite people handle stomach gas at table, their faces sick with restraint.

Around that time I overheard Jean discussing a family friend. "He's that one in a million who can plain get away with things. Escapades the rest of us—well, we wouldn't dare, that's all." It was said with a certain affectionate dismay. From this I extrapolated that Leo must be one in another million, with special privileges under heaven. "Rat face," he called Drake, and when Patty joined the group he'd hold his nose, saying, "I smell dog." Both these kids were older, in junior high. Why didn't they just pop him one?

Among Leo's sundry armaments was an outsized unsharpened advertising pencil from his father's office. L.J. ENGRAVING, it said, in letters that looked burned into the wood.

Hiding the giant pencil in his sleeve, Leo would pace the tarmac, whistling, waiting; then, the very instant I relaxed my watch, he would charge. This mischief was all the more painful as spring wore on and I wore less and less. "Ow!" I'd holler. "Hey!" And Leo would throw up his arms, one of them stiff as a fence post, in startled innocence. For weeks that spring my tender white body bloomed with tattoo-like rosettes in all the subtle values from injury through healing.

Appalled, Jean made a series of telephone calls to Mrs. Jacoby. But if Leo was punished, it didn't show. So Jean began to keep me indoors until the very last second. Around this time my father cut back to a three-day work week. He needed time, he said, "to prepare my flower bed and rest my elderly bones." He often kicked off these leisure days by driving me to school.

He'd always been an amenable sort, but I sensed on these occasions an even deeper willingness, an almost joyful surrender of edges. With a predatory instinct at least as keen as Leo's, I took shameless advantage of my father. Each day, when I saw the Dairyland approach, I put in a noisy bid for a Dixie Cup.

In memory, the first time I made this demand, it landed on his face like a horsefly. He slapped his cheek and sighed, peered hard at oncoming traffic, as if his argument were with it. Then, "Heck," he said, "what's ice cream anyhow?" "Air and milk!" he told the passing motorists, tight inside themselves. "Hey, air is essential for life, milk for healthy bones and teeth. Think a minute, Ben," he said, addressing his mirror image. "When you really analyze things, really get down to it, hey, what's so blasted wrong with being late for school?" From this small but delectable revelation his body seemed to rise, visibly lighter, and because by then we'd already passed the Dairyland, he went squealing through the Texaco station to avoid the light and then zipped up an alley and around the block.

His "game" was insurance—his word, of course, spoken with a hearty, transforming pride. I grew up considering insurance the highest goal a man could aspire to. Proud of his work, his family, of every gewgaw and gadget he owned, my father liked to call himself "a lucky devil." "Lucky Me," in fact, was *his* song; he used to hum it so much it drove us half crazy. Jean had no song. She just wasn't the type you'd try to link up with a pop tune.

Once, on the way to school, he refused to buy me a Clark bar, as a matter of principle—*Jean's* principle, for she believed firmly that chocolate was toxic before twelve noon. He hated to say no. When I stopped importuning, he told me a strange story. "This is about a very *unlucky* fellow," he said. "Young man, never been in any type of trouble before, decided out of the blue to go out and steal a car. He was basically a good kid, with an itch to do a little something bad. For the heck of it." My father swiveled right, bugging his dark eyes, his way of beaming forth a story's highlights.

"Grabbed one from right there," he said, as we pulled abreast of the local post office. "The idea, you see, was to take a little spin and then return the vehicle while there was still time on the meter. Well, our boy was tooling along some country road, thinking, what a kicker, when he heard some mighty peculiar noises in the back seat. Well, he finally decided to take a peek back there. And what do you suppose he saw?"

"A mallard," I said, because *mallard* was a funny word.

"Nope," he said. "A baby girl. Not even a month old, wrapped in a pink blanket. Our boy hadn't bothered to check for cargo. The baby's mama was in the post office, mailing a package to her young hubby, who was off fighting somewhere in Europe. In fifteen short minutes this kid had gone from your basic good egg to the lowest human form, a kidnapper . . . ."

"They sent him to Morganza, right?" I assumed he'd told that story as a cautionary tale, figuring that a kid who carried on so over a Clark bar could easily grow up to be a car thief. But my question went unaddressed. The man beside me wore a deeply private smile. I think he was just being philosophical that day, amazing himself with how life could turn out, and then go right on turning.

One morning Jean decided to come along. "Hey, great!" my father said. "We'll take the day off, all three of us." "Partners in crime," he teased. This three-way truancy represented a giant leap for Jean, given her age and tendencies. To my surprise she said, "Just once wouldn't hurt, I s'pose. But just this once, mind you."

First we drove out to a small farm and got some cuttings for his mums. The bed was already prepared. It was a small plot into which he'd spaded rich black dirt, everything raked to a grainy fineness.

From there we went to Gardenland for supplies. As usual

my father did the salesman's job for him. "Your five-ten-five—won't burn the roots. Better stuff than the Sears brand, right? How do your prices compare generally? Unbeatable, huh? Well, you get what you pay for."

At all this the salesman nodded, Jean observing, with adoring disbelief, the predictable ways of the man she had married, this good man who nudged people into comforting lies about themselves.

After lunch someone suggested Fun City, a dilapidated park not far from home. Most of the rides had long been idle by then, but mothers still brought pre-schoolers to the swing set and to a toothless man with ponies—a sad, scabby lot, pawing at the packed earth, not wanting to be bothered. My father gave the man two quarters: one of his ponies would carry me thrice around a walking trail for fifty cents. My parents walked on either side of the creature, each of them gripping me, a skittish city kid, around the waist. Nervously, I kept swiveling back and forth, and after all these years I still feel I caught the two of them at something: their eyes were fixed on each other, their fingers entwined as if I, Jeremiah, were merely a legitimate excuse to touch in public.

Except for the brat, ours was a serene neighborhood, one of those subdivisions begun after the war but before the days of false brick and vinyl siding. With a matter-of-fact profligacy we covered varnished oak with hi-lo carpeting and accepted as our due the ceramic tile, the stone hearth, the mud room, the rumpus room, the all-birch kitchen. In addition to a finished basement our house boasted a wide center hall and what they called a half-attic—a small, angular room with a sealed round window, like a ship's porthole, that the former owners had fixed up for a maiden aunt. Our neighbors were fanatical about upkeep, and we were doing our level best to keep up.

"It was a mistake," my father said one evening, meaning the purchase of our excellent house. He'd been outside, trying to finish mowing before dark. He'd collapsed, exhausted, on the couch. The same with painting trim a week later. In his intense, meticulous way he'd been inching around the mullions when his arm started to shake. Enormous sweat globules stood on his brow as Jean helped him off the step stool and led him inside. His skin had a harsh bluish cast that made his features seem pasted in place. With longish, thinning hair, he looked like an old woman, I saw. He looked like his wife, gray herself and delicate from indoor living.

She, meaning well, attempted to finish these tasks. What can I say? The mower stalled. She didn't know how to restart it. One day Mr. Jacoby offered to help but, perhaps sensing some hidden fee, she said, "Thank you, no." She hated painting—the tedium, the mess. "We'll have to get someone. But who. *Who?*" she mumbled, looking around, as if that's how one went about locating a yardman. In this new place we were all children.

Across the street the Stuvers were adding on. For many months that spring a staggered stack of yellow bricks stood like courthouse steps in their side yard. The setup was ideal for King of the Hill, which I often played alone, fantasizing Apaches but looking for Leo, hoping for him, whom I would now lord over and laugh at and vanquish. One Saturday, as I stood surveying my domain, pondering my how-cans and what-ifs, he sneaked up on my blind side and swept me off the ledge like a speck of dust. My ankle cracked in two places.

From the emergency room we went directly to Leo's house. At the door Jean shook my crutches like a fist while my father thrust me up, incontestable proof, our right of entry.

I remember that their front room was empty except for a bean-bag chair, a yucca plant, and an upright white piano. Mrs. Jacoby was quick to explain the paucity. "We're waiting," she said, glancing cautiously at her husband, "till we can afford to do it right." Mr. Jacoby hurried out of the room and returned with tall glasses of iced tea.

"I'd rather have soda pop," I said.

My father poked me, but Mr. Jacoby said, "Hey," and produced, in short order, a can of cold Coke.

The Jacobys wore solemn faces, but no, I cannot say they looked sorry. The three of us were lined up in front of the fireplace, which contained now, in April, a basket of plastic flowers. Between my parents I listed to the right like Tiny Tim.

In a peasant blouse and denim mini-skirt, Mrs. Jacoby stood a full generation away from Jean, whose rayon print fell primly to mid-calf. The younger woman's hand on my back was more a taking-charge than an act of sympathy or contrition.

"Needless to say," she said, "Lisle and I regret very much that this had to happen."

"Had to?" Jean crossed her arms. Her chin dipped severely.

"Listen, maybe there's something you should know before you"—Mr. Jacoby paused—"go off half-cocked." His large, sculpted head seemed to belong on a larger man's body, or on a famous statue.

They were direct in this, businesslike, unblinking. Mrs. Jacoby said, "I'm surprised nobody's told you."

"Two full months we've been here," Jean said. "And hardly a body's gone out of their way to say how-do, let alone fill us in."

"These days," Mr. Jacoby said, edging close to his wife, "people have distractions."

"We live day to day," his wife said.

At this my parents stiffened, sniffed as if alerted, as if they were about to be gobbled up or done out of something.

"Leonard's IQ is one of the highest ever recorded in the school district," Mrs. Jacoby blurted, out of left field.

My father drew a breath so deep it graveled his tone. "Pardon me, ma'am, but how does IQ figure—"

With a gesture I now see as smug and presumptuous, Mr. Jacoby raised a splayed hand. *Stop*, he seemed to be saying. *For your own good, give it up now*. When the tension in the room was right—in the silence—he said, "Our son is dying." Mrs. Jacoby held Jean's eyes with a long, unwavering gaze.

We left in clumping confusion. Thoughtful across the yards, we stopped to check my father's cuttings, which sweated in their little fruit-jar greenhouses. We went in the back way, where, on the white walls of the mud room, the late light lay condensed to ingots of deep gold.

Jean's self-control was such that all she ever showed of rage was its surfeit, the stuff too much for her craw, what escaped from between her teeth. One unmistakable sign of fury was a shift in tempo, so that suddenly she'd be vacuuming with the speed of a silent movie. Or racing the dishes off the table. Or, as now, in the still unfamiliar house, humping around, switching on lights, rattling bags, opening and shutting the oven, mumbling, muttering. In the meantime, my father hovered and bumbled around her, like some clumsy dog who'd done wrong. Finally he just reached out and snagged her close, steering her this way and that until the two of them, like a single wounded beast, began to weave down the hall to their bedroom, which had been moved in recent weeks from the second floor to the downstairs den. Outraged, I made my own way to bed, faking a clattering fall in the hallway to show how resoundingly they'd failed as parents.

In retrospect, I see that the other thing between them and me was knowledge. Over time that knowledge has taken on a solid look, has lodged in memory like something black on an x-ray. That's how very sick my father was at the time. The Jacobys had cut deeper into us that day than they had intended. My father's frenzied solicitude toward Jean was an effort to make it up to her. For himself. For Leo. For the fact that we were all hostages to these dying people.

As for Leo, well, who can say that given a longer life, he wouldn't have spent it burglarizing rest homes or slandering his faithful wife in singles bars. But we—everybody—gave him the benefit and hated ourselves for it. In the weeks that followed, my father began spending more and more time in the hospital or home in bed. Jean was occupied with duty or dread. So I mostly rode the disgusting bus. Leo ate my double-dessert lunches en route, defaced my homework. He'd been in remission, his parents had said, nearly a year. I think we thought of him as hosting an elaborate internal menace. One shake and we'd wake up a nest of army ants, who'd be all over him in seconds.

Every Sunday at exactly five the three of us sat down to a fat capon. After one of these meals Jean laid down her fork and looked hard at my father. "Has it occurred to you that maybe the Jacobys are ly—*mistaken*? That boy looks hale enough to me."

"Cures are not unheard of," he said, lifting an orange from the fruit bowl. For a second her eyes on him shone, impudent with hope, but he was busy with the orange, his trembling fingers digging at the rind, dropping it, trying again. Jean blinked and took the orange away. "Jerry, don't rock back on your chair," she said, as she proceeded to skin that orange alive.

My crutches. Having quickly mastered them, I rode them in high style, as if they were circus stilts, or a unicycle. They were my ticket to privilege and tender regard. They worked their magic everywhere but with Leo, to whom these appliances, with their six weeks' useful life, must have seemed symbolic less of disability than of repair: *I* would heal. One morning in late May, as I stood with the bus crowd, Leo took them. Recently he'd spent some time in the hospital and had returned hairless and skinny, prone to throwing up on the bus.

Today I know what the effort must have cost him. Mr. Jacoby, who'd been replacing cedar shakes, had left an aluminum ladder standing against the house. Somehow managing to juggle his book bag, his lunch, and my crutches, Leo scrabbled up the ladder. At the top he tossed the crutches onto the garage roof. He then descended, hauled the ladder into the garage, and still found strength to drag down the heavy track door. Utterly bereft, I sat down on the macadam and hollered my head off.

And Jean came running. Halfway across the front lawn she stopped. That moment of hesitation, I'm sure, is even longer in memory than in fact. But she was Jean. Surely she would have wrestled with herself a second or two, her fingers drumming, tugging on their invisible strings. Defiant to the jawbone, Leo was taunting her now with his arms crossed. Then, sensing something excessive (and grown unappeasable) in her, he lunged for the post that held our two mailboxes, grabbing hold with both hands. The other children stood like trees with their leaves turned against bad weather. Nothing good would come of this. They expected the worst, in fact; they expected to be embarrassed.

In the meantime Jean was struggling, straining against what must have been the stolid, obstructing arm of civilization itself. Then, chopping at the air, with a small, catlike cry of surprise, she charged, flying at Leo, detaching him from his stanchion as effortlessly as she tore cobwebs from rafters.

This ease must have amazed her most of all, and she hesitated another endless second before taking his shoulders and shaking that sick boy until I thought his shiny head would fly off.

This next part I cannot swear to. It happened either in fact or in a dream or both: Mrs. Jacoby's face at an upstairs window. She is clutching something to her—a pillow? A cloth toy? The early light is shellacking the glass, but I sense her despair just before she turns away, for she had finally run dry.

Not so my father. Where had *he* come from? In bedroom slippers and robe he was on the move, shuffling across the grass, his arm out like a penalty call. When he reached the combatants, he circled left, right, ducking, hacking at Jean's arm before taking a two-fisted, infantile grip on the back of her belt. In his condition he was no match for a provoked female, but he gained some leverage by bracing himself against a fence rail, from which position he tugged at her as someone might restrain a horse. In a voice soft as chalk, he said, "Damn it, Jean, get the hell in the house."

He was so insubstantial and she so heedless that I cannot believe his efforts registered. When she finally let go, it was because she was spent, or because the unseemliness of it all had caught up with her. Suddenly she was throwing her arms out from her, as if disaffiliating herself from them. Then, drawing herself up tall and schoolmarmish, she stood a long time, just squinting up the street. "The bus," she said. She went in then, leaving my father and Leo linked, hand to elbow, as if they were about to cross a busy street. They were both bald, blazingly white in the morning sun. Clothes hanging, bones poking through, they were the spitting image of each other. They could have been father and son.

Thursday of that week was Leo's last day of school. That night he was rushed to the hospital, and from there, well, nobody knew exactly. Years later, when I asked, Jean said they had buried him furtively, like a mistake—no viewing, no funeral. I didn't tell her that at the time she had said he went to Morganza; that to this day the words *mortal* and *incorrigible* are synonymous to me and that I look upon dying as a capital offense, the only crime aside from jealousy that is, at once, its own punishment.

My father lasted through the summer and into the early days of autumn. His mums came into bloom in time to make a pungent funeral bouquet. They looked spectacular to me, but, what with everything else, they never made it to the contest.

He was ambitious for one so frail. Twice that summer he moved, the first time on his own steam, lugging, over Jean's nearly hysterical objections, his Sunday suit, Boy Scout Handbook, and down pillow from the den to their old room, the master bedroom on the second floor. A month later, in the swelter of August, he insisted on moving to the attic. This time Jean asked Mr. Stuver to help get my single bed up the narrow steps. They tucked it under the eaves, under the round window, which presided over that dim little space like a maniacally cheerful sky-blue moon. Having lost my bed, I moved to the guest room. Everything was getting shuffled; my father was leaving a level at a time.

During those last months he could not bear the lovely sight of his life's partner. "Jean," he'd say, "I smell something burning." "Jean, the phone." My leg had healed, freeing me to take full advantage. Gladly I ran up and down the steps, best friend now to both parents. In a manly—no, *husbandly*—way I held forth about the weather and the headlines, while helping Jean with the almost sacramental task of tending my father's garden. I showed the visiting nurse to the attic, read to my father, and acted as courier, carrying messages from her who could on some days barely deliver them out of her mouth.

Somehow I must have intuited that what I was about to lose went beyond my paternal root to something deeper, the root of that root, my father's memory. I asked him questions nobody else could answer, about his parents, his grandparents, his life before Jean.

"What else about Grampy?"

"Oh, did I mention his watch? It was big and round, with all seven planets on its face."

"Silver or gold?"

"Rolled gold—better than plate."

The room retained the aromatic smell of newish wood, which the heat deepened to something that made me think of incense. On the single straight wall hung a print left by the room's last occupant. In it a pretty, flaxen-haired child held a luminous dove. It was mounted in an oval Victorian frame.

"Were you a delinquent? Like Leo?"

My father cackled. "I was a little priss," he said. "At three, when my mother took me to visit the neighbors, I checked their ledges for dust. I straightened their rugs."

"Yuck."

All those weeks, even as I enjoyed my improved status, my privileged visitorhood, I must have sensed the true significance of the new order, that the current gulf between my parents was only another measure of their intimacy. Day by day I felt growing in me a terrible meanness, an inexplicable rage. "And what was the dog's name?" I asked for the twentieth time.

"Luke, " he said.

"What happened to old Luke?" As if I didn't know.

"He got hit by a meat wagon," my father said. He could have said the dog was killed, and left it at that. But no, he always added the silly part about the meat wagon, slapping it on like mud on a bee sting.

"Splat," I said, giggling.

But my father wasn't finished. "I bawled my head off, you know." Breathless now, he struggled to an upright position. The room was like an oven, and his lips were parched, even as he shivered with chill. I poured him some ice water, quickly, so as not to miss a word. This part was new to me.

" 'Don't cry,' my mama said. 'Just remember, Benjamin, someday you'll see Luke in heaven with Jesus and His angels.' But my grammy was there that day. She was the sharp kind, like your mother. 'Good God, Addy, don't tell him that,' she said. 'Dogs don't have souls. Luke is done for.' "

My father's head jerked back and he looked up at me, astonished. An instant later he went vague, precarious, and just as I thought he might cry, I blurted, "I'll tell you who's done for. Old Leo is done for. It's a dirty lie he's in Morganza. He's down there—" I pointed to the braided rug. "Leo's shoveling coal with his big pencil. Leo's making snowballs in hell."

"Jerry!"

"Leo's picking his nose in hell." I giggled some more. "Leo puts out flames with piss." I went on like that, and when I could no longer outdo myself in grossness, irreverence, and spite, I looked up. "Is that so wrong of me?"

"All things considered?" he said. "Yes, I should say it is."

"Good, I'm glad," I said, crawling across my old bed to a spot by the round blue window. Outside, the grass was going ragged with late summer, housewives on webbed lounges lay baking in the sun, their kids squealing without sound in round blue plastic pools that echoed the window in which I, absolutely still and thinking my thoughts, felt embedded. What I was thinking about was death and Leo and me, in that order. I saw all three of us at once, the way a cartoonist might depict a dog chasing a cat chasing a mouse. Then Leo was overtaken. Leo and death became one runner, and that's how I kept Leo alive—as he will be all my life. He is the one I look for over my shoulder, as I had done the day I played King of the Hill, as I was doing at that moment, perched on my father's anklebones, surveying the green kingdom of my childhood.

I got on my knees then and pressed closer, nose to the glass, until the street, directly below, reeled into my vision. Our locust tree. The deft suggestion of fence. And down there, by the double mailbox, Jean and Mrs. Jacoby, each fanning herself with a packet of letters, their heads nodding, their free hands touching. I watched the women with suspicious eyes. They'll be friends, I thought bitterly.

One rainy Saturday in late September, I sat watching my father emerge from drugged sleep. Those last weeks each time he awoke, he looked perplexed and then, after orienting himself, disappointed for a while, before a sort of grim acceptance set in. I waited out all his stages before putting my question to him. "And what happened to the boy who stole the baby? You never said."

He began to soften, as he had those mornings in the car, when he'd hit upon an excuse to buy me ice cream for breakfast. His wasted face bloomed with relief. "Nothing bad, mind you," he said. "He brought the baby back immediately. The law showed mercy. He and the young woman became very good friends, and when her husband was killed in the war, he married her and the three of them moved to another town."

I looked at him, his eyes burning in deep purple holes, his skin ungodly bright. So it must be, Leo, when the light from a man's deepest soul becomes a shallow thing. The law showed mercy, Leo, and the rain was a kind of grace as I clambered over his legs to take my place at the round window.

Down below, the driveway is awash, three pre-schoolers

high-stepping through in tulip-colored boots. I look at the staggered rooftops rising to the top street and think, Not *neighborhood* but *village*, the rain silvers everything so, dulls the hopeful colors, makes us all beautifully old. I can't see your house from here, but in the rainy-day dark of it your parents are making desperate love. Everything is fluid, moving, nothing prevails, not even my meanness. Look at the lawns and late flowers, low clouds and tangled streets, the sheets left on the Tysons' line, my selfishness indistinguishable now from sorrow: and death, gently blending in, altering forever the smell of the attic.

From behind me then came a thin strand of sound, low and broken. I thought he was moaning and, frozen, I could not turn to him at first. Minutes passed, the rain drummed down, and in the same instant that I recognized the tune, it came to me, like shocking news, that on this day of measured time I, Jeremiah, was still a child. I left the window and went to him, driving myself tight against the bony harp that was my father's body. He went on humming my song, stopping often for breath, until we both went to sleep.

Leo, Leo, my incorrigible friend. Joy to you. And me.

"Leo" Discussion

1. This story is a childhood memory that is told from the perspective and experience of that same child, all grown up. Jeremiah the child believed his family moved to Shepherd Hills so his father could raise "mums" (chrysanthemums) for a flower show. What does Jeremiah the adult now recognize as the reason for their move?
2. What kind of parents are Ben and Jean, and how does that affect the way they handle Leo's bullying?
3. How does Jeremiah's relationship to his parents change by the end of the story?

4. When Leo's parents tell Ben and Jean their son is dying, Jeremiah the child believes they are too easily defeated by the news. What does Jeremiah the adult recognize now about that news?
5. Why does Jean lose all control with Leo in the scene where he puts Jeremiah's crutches on the roof?
6. Why does Mrs. Jacoby (either in reality or in Jeremiah's memory) turn away from the sight of Jean shaking her son?
7. Why do you suppose Jean and Mrs. Jacoby become friends?
8. When Ben moves to the attic and he and Jean are no longer together all the time, Jeremiah observes " . . . that the current gulf between my parents was only another measure of their intimacy." What does he mean by this?
9. Why does Jeremiah laugh at the thought of his father's dog getting run over and the thought of Leo in hell?
10. Were you moved at the end of this story? What does Jeremiah understand now that he did not before?

Suggestion for Writing

Think of an event from your childhood about which your perceptions have changed over time. Write about these events, and try to compare the feelings you had at the time with how you feel now, looking back.

Lucy Cowgirl

by Jacquie Giasson Fuller

(First appeared in Yankee*)*

In this quiet story about a mother and daughter, the images tell the tale. As you read, you might ask yourself: What does it mean to have roots? Does a person's future begin when she acknowledges her past? For the two women in this story, the past and future converge in one poignant moment.

About the Author

JACQUIE GIASSON FULLER is a part-time English instructor at the University of Southern Maine. Her poems, essays, and short stories have appeared in magazines and periodicals throughout New England. She is currently working on a novel about Franco-Americans that takes place in her hometown of Lewiston, Maine. Of the writing process, she observes: "What I've come to understand is that a writer is simply someone who writes; it doesn't matter that the work . . . won't reach a wide audience, although if one is willing to persist that's certainly possible. I write for the same reasons now as I did back in high school—because it's enjoyable and helps me to make sense of this ever-confusing world."

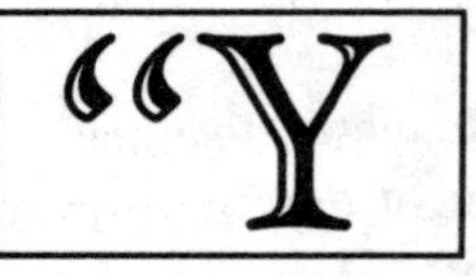

"You can be French and be a cowgirl, too," I say, when I'm pulling on my boots.

Linny laughs and rolls her brown eyes—those ones she got from me—right around in her head, like she's checking all four corners of the earth to see if anyone's listening to the dumb things her mother's saying.

Linnie's 17 now, almost grown up. Growing away from me.

"It ain't the French part," she says in that voice that comes more out her nose than her mouth. (That she got from her father—"It ain't the playin' in bars, Lucy," Fern would say through his nose. "It's the idea of a wife of mine wearin' a cowgirl suit.")

That's why we been alone together a long time, Linnie and me. So happens the only time I can call up Fern's face anymore is when she's whining at me.

"It ain't the French part," she says. "It's the INDIAN part. How can you put yourself in cowgirl clothes?"

"*Voyons*. I'm a lot more French than I am Indian," I say. I'm standing in front of the mirror on my medicine cabinet, buttoning my blue satin shirt with the red piping.

"Besides, I sing cowboy songs," I tell her, looking at the reflection of them brown-black eyes. "What am I gonna do, put on an Indian suit and sing 'Help Me Make It Through the Night?' People at Ti-Bozo's are gonna think I went nuts."

Linnie tries not to laugh. She goes out in the living room and leans out the window. From the third floor we can see Ti-Bozo's big neon sign real plain.

"Good crowd outside?" I yell out the bathroom door.

"Lotsa COWBOYS," she says, using Fern's voice.

This is how we go on, Linnie and me, every Friday and Saturday night when I get ready for gigs. Been so ever since last year when I made the mistake of telling her she's got Maine Indian in her.

I cooked a can of fiddleheads one day. I opened the can and plopped them things in the pot and Linnie picks up the can and sniffs at it.

"How can you eat that pukey stuff?" she goes. "Smells like spinach."

"Well, I ate it growin' up," I say. "So did you. You ate it right up when you was my *p'tite bébé*, big smile on your face."

"How the hell do you know that?" Linnie shoots back.

Left myself wide open there. Linnie wouldn't miss an opportunity like that.

Guess maybe me and Fern shouldn't have had a baby. But how do you know 'til you got one? 'Cause I been Lucy Cowgirl since the day I was born. It's always been the music, music and dancing; that's what does the world good. That's what God wants. All I want to do is make people happy, make 'em feel good.

When Linnie was little, I did gigs up and down, Augusta to North Conway, places in between. Me and the band on the road in the VW bus, five-six nights a week, sleeping 'til noon the day after. We made damn good money, but Linnie got carted around, woke most mornings not knowing where she was, where I was.

One day I come home from a weekend gig and she toddles up and latches onto my leg. I don't know she can walk.

"Of course she's walkin'," my mama says. "She's been walkin' for a week now."

Felt bad about that. So I let her take a shot at me now and then. Why not? Figure I got it coming.

Anyway, I tell her *Pepère Grenier* told me his great-grandma gave him fiddleheads and dandelions to eat, and she was pure Maine Indian.

"So that means we got some in us," I told her.

"We do?" she goes, and her brown eyes start doing funny things, changing colors and popping around in her head.

"We got pictures of her smokin' a pipe in her rocking chair," I say.

"We do?" she says, her eyes lighting up like flashbulbs.

The next day she visits *Memère Grenier* and brings home the pictures and Linnie shows me how that ol' squaw has them same brown eyes we got.

"Christ, I LOOK like her," Linnie says, and I let the blasphemy go by. "*Memère* don't remember her name, and it don't say on the back. You think any of the *n'oncles* or the *tantes* would know?"

I shake my head. My daughter's got her hair in a long braid in the back and it's true, she looks like the squaw.

Then Linnie goes weird over Indians.

"I can really see it in me," she says the other day. She's been saving pigeon feathers she finds on the sidewalk outside the apartment building, and she keeps them in a box, tucks them in her braid like they're hairs stuck in a big zipper, ten-twelve at a time.

She's imitating pigeon noises, cooing all over the place. It gets on my nerves.

"But that's what they used to do, right?" Linnie goes. "In the ol' Westerns. You see cowboys around the fire at night, talkin' in them low voices, and you hear an owl noise: WHO-WHO-WHO-WHO-WHO! And you know it's Indians. You almost wanta yell, 'Look out, cowboys! There's Indians all around you!' But those cowboys are so dumb. They jus' keep talkin' about their ranches."

"That's true," I tell her.

"Indians knew the land. And ain't that true for me? Don't I know all the alley shortcuts? Don't I know how to move around in the city?"

"That's a good point," I says.

When I put on my string tie with the blue nugget, Linnie says, "Ma, that's INJUN jewelry," and she hugs me real hard. She hands me my hat and I put it on, staring right at her face, now she's as tall as me. The big braid's pulling her hair back tight. She's got good skin, good teeth, no make-up—she's beautiful. I hand her my guitar.

"Might come see you tonight," she says, while she tunes it up. I'm surprised to hear that. "You know I hate country-western, but I ain't heard you sing in a long time," she says softly.

You never know what'll come out a teenager's mouth.

"Well, you're underage," I says. "But I'll tell Ti-Bozo you're comin'."

Ti-Bozo's ain't a bad place to play. Crowd of about 75 on a good night, and in a mill town it's always a good night. Noise gets outa hand sometimes. Then I jus' go on automatic, since no one hears it anyway—put the power and the warble in their place so I can look around and dream. I can almost see the words I'm singing run up past my face and disappear over my head, like steam outa hot stew.

What'll I do, cry? Cowgirls don't, or they shouldn't, especially on a Saturday night, 'cause even if the crowd is restless, they shouldn't have a crying woman to think about on a Saturday night, when they're stuck on a noisy machine, working hard, all week. That's the way I see it.

After "Make the World Go Away" there's some claps, mostly from my gang at the right-hand table, who come to listen, and I say into the mike, "Thank you, thank you much. I'm Lucy Cowgirl, and I'm happy to take your requests."

A punk-haired kid, 25, 26, sends up a napkin. He wants

"On the Road Again." Jeez, I'm tired of that tune, but it turns out to be a good idea, 'cause just about everyone gets up and begins to move their feet, which is what I like to see.

After that one, I get passed an anonymous note by Ti-Bozo. It says "Running Bear."

"Sorry," I say in the mike. "I ain't sung that in a million years. Let me do this one for y'all instead." (I say y'all only when I'm working. Don't seem natural at home.)

I do "Quand Le Soleil Dit Bonjour Aux Montagnes" for ol' *Monsieur Hēbert* in front—I been keeping track of him all night. Drinks too much since he got widowed. So I look right at him and make it gentle and caressing, like a lullabye, see if I can brighten up them sad eyes.

Everyone keeps talking while I do the French part, and then at the English verse someone gets up. I stop singing, mouth wide open, when I see it's Linnie moving out onto the floor, but I catch myself and go on.

"*When the sun says good day to the mountains*," I sing, and Linnie begins to sway. She's wearing Fern's ol' brown suede jacket with the long fringes. Don't know how she got it away from him; Fern loved that ol' coat. She has the pigeon feathers tucked in her braid, and she's not wearing shoes, which worries me a bit, considering what you might find on the floor.

"*And the night says hello to the dawn*," I sing, not hearing myself from the noise and from being surprised. Linnie spreads her arms out like they're wings, and she starts spinning around, so that she looks like an eagle trying to lift up off the ground, wounded maybe, suffering. It—she has a look on her face like she's just been shot and ain't ready to go down yet. She circles round and round.

I sing, "*I'm alone with my dreams on the hilltop*," and Linnie turns and twists, and the punk-haired boy gets up and begins to jerk himself around in front of her.

Linnie spins some more, then she stops, almost falling. I can see she's dizzy, looking around, trying to hold herself up. The punk-boy never stops throwing his body around, them long arms and legs of his orbiting around the dance floor. I jus' keep strumming the tune.

"*I can still hear his voice though he's gone.*"

Then I lean sideways over my guitar. "Dance!" I say, keeping my voice out of the mike, calling to Linnie over the heads of the people screaming to talk to each other. "Dance! It's beautiful!"

Some people notice what I'm saying and begin clapping, egging her on. Linnie circles them brown eyes like a spotlight on the faces in the crowd, and then she puts them on me.

Feathers are peeking out the side of Linnie's head, and the fringed jacket reaches down to her knees. But my daughter's beautiful, standing there. Indian maiden, is what I think of.

Another couple gets up, goes out on the floor and starts waltzing. I keep strumming my song, the song I been singing years and years.

"*I hear from my door the love song through the wind,*
It brings back sweet memories of you."

Linnie's looking at me and she smiles a smile so big it shuts up her eyes. She lifts one bare foot high up in the air, like she's about to take her first step all over again.

And this time, this time I watch.

"Lucy Cowgirl" Discussion

1. This story is full of vivid images. Find some of these images and briefly state how they help define the characters and setting.

2. The bar that Lucy sings in is a run-down, working-class bar. How do we know this?

3. What kind of relationship does Lucy have with Linnie? Find examples from the story to support your answer.
4. Why do you suppose Linnie is so pleased to be part Indian?
5. Why do you suppose Lucy encourages Linnie to make a spectacle of herself in the bar?
6. Very often, short stories capture a turning point, a significant moment after which nothing will ever be the same. Is that true here? If so, what is that "moment" and what do you think it means to the characters?
7. How does Linnie change between the moment she discovers her Indian heritage and her final dance on the floor of the bar?
8. The story begins with Lucy saying, "You can be French and be a cowgirl, too." In some ways this story is about being more than one person at once: a girl and a woman, French and Indian, for instance. Discuss what it means to be from one culture and live in another, or to be part of a minority culture. Have you ever had such an experience? Have you ever felt as if you had more than one identity?

Suggestion for Writing

Setting in this story is important: Lucy is a Franco-American (a person whose family emigrated from French-speaking Canada) living in Maine. Franco-Americans, especially in New England, have a rich heritage. Ask your parents or other family members about your own heritage, and write a story or essay describing what you learned.

Certain Elements

by Dawn Raffel

(First appeared in
The North American Review)

Two sisters. A night on the town. On one level, this small tale is as simple as that. But beneath her fierce and hungry description of a worldly yet vulnerable older sister, the narrator tells another, far more complicated story of a thick sisterly bond, and a twelve-year-old's insatiable desire to walk in the murky world of adulthood.

About the Author

DAWN RAFFEL was raised in Milwaukee, Wisconsin, and now lives with her husband in New York City where she is the fiction editor of *Redbook*. Her stories have appeared in several literary magazines and anthologies. Of "Certain Elements" Dawn writes: "The story is a mixture of memory, exaggeration, and wishful thinking. I wanted to capture the moment of feeling yourself right on the cusp of enormous change, when the world seems most full of mystery and possibility."

nn wanted me to fork over. I was in my room, listening to Ro-zee radio and painting my fingernails Moonglow, and the sign on my door said Knock and Be Recognized, but this meant nothing to my sister. She had an identical sign scotch-taped to her door but hers meant business.

"How much cash do you have?" she asked, turning down the volume on my radio. "I've got to blow this pop stand." It was Friday, just after dinner; she was pacing. "Come on, how much are you worth?"

"Oh, I don't know," I said. "Maybe eight, maybe ten dollars. Something like that." In fact I had $22.70 in allowances and birthday money crumpled in an apothecary jar in my underwear drawer. I wasn't exactly hiding my money, but I didn't want anyone to know how much I had, either. It was like the candy bar the cleaning lady gave us every Wednesday: I buried mine deep under my nighties just in case. Ann always ate hers right away and a few days later she'd remember mine and make me give her half.

"I'll bet you know exactly how much you have," Ann said. "I'll bet you have $30 or $40."

I shook my head.

"Look, I just need a loan, is all," she said.

"Where are you going?"

"That's for me to know and you not to."

These were some of the places Ann went on the weekends: Nick's Nickobob, where she and her friend Alouette got served whiskey sours even though they were seventeen, on account of Alouette's boobs; the Echo Bowling Lanes, where the greaser chicks crowded the bathroom mirror so they could put on more eyeliner; the downtown arcade, which was ritzy before I was born. Technically, our parents had forbidden all of these, but what really worried them was the arcade, because of Certain Elements. This meant Ann's ex-boyfriend Phil, who worked grill at the Big Boy on the first floor. The one time I met him he seemed shy and polite but he was 23 and had his license suspended for reckless endangerment. Our parents suspected Ann still saw him and they were right.

I had a mental picture of each of Ann's hangouts, even though I'd only been to the Echo Bowl once and Nick's Nickobob never. In my mind they were all dark with a sort of red tint, like the hall of bats at the zoo. The places I went with my friends—Daffy Fashions and Whoops! and the counter at Walgreen's—were bright as a television.

I hardly ever spent money—if I needed a nail polish or something I just slipped it into my pocket—and Ann knew I always had a cash supply. She rarely paid me back, but the next day she'd toss me some scrap of information: What Alouette said when the barman put the moves on her for the millionth time or what movie she saw with Certain Elements. She always told me just enough so I felt gypped.

I'd been thinking that just once it would be nice to get my money's worth and on the spur of the moment, I decided to outsmart her.

"Here's the deal," I said. "I'll lend you twelve dollars—"

"Thanks," she said.

"—But only if I can come with."

"*What?*" She rolled her eyes. "Look, you can't come. Just give me the money, O.K., and I'll pay you back tomorrow."

"Fat chance. You already owe me six dollars."

"So what are you, my goddamn twelve-year-old accountant?"

"You want the money or not?" I asked.

Ann put a hand on her hip, considering. She ran her fingers through her thick black hair, which she'd stopped brushing, which drove our mother crazy. She'd also gained about thirty pounds in the last year and wore the same dress—a blue tent with one orange stripe and a few cigarette burns—almost every day.

"Well?" I asked.

"There's not a snowball's chance in hell Mom and Dad'll let you go with me," she said. "Watch. We'll ask, O.K., and they'll say no."

The minute we pulled out of the driveway, Ann lit up. Then she offered me a cigarette—cig, she said—and lit it for me. I rolled down the window and tried not to inhale too much; this was my third cig ever.

These were the terms of my going with Ann: No Nickobob—I'd never get in, anyway—no socializing with Certain Elements, home by nine sharp or be grounded. Mom hated letting Ann drive her Buick, but she always gave in; otherwise Ann would just hitchhike, sticking out like a sore thumb in our subdivision.

Ann steered with her left hand, adjusted the radio dial with her right and turned up the volume. When we came to a stoplight, she waited until the last second, then hit the brakes hard so the tires screeched. I threw my cig out the window and pictured how an accident would look, blood dripping off the dashboard.

"Where are we going?" I asked.

"To hell," Ann said, in her best Transylvanian older sister voice.

Finding a parking space near the arcade took a long time; Ann couldn't parallel. I hadn't been in the arcade in two years, since I'd had a cyst removed at the plastic surgeon's across the street. Afterwards our mother bought me a box of caramel corn from a wagon near the Big Boy. I still remembered how good that corn tasted, but we hadn't stayed: Mom wanted to get out of that neighborhood before dark.

The arcade ran the length of a double block and had a marble staircase as wide as a boulevard. Miss Clement's School of Poise and Beauty had been there a million years, and a few old shops still sold things like corsets. But the newer stores dealt in trashy-looking dresses and spike heels and donuts, and the whole place had a sort of stale circus smell. The Big Boy was carved into a corner, with both an arcade and an all-night street entrance.

We sat at the counter and ordered a Coke each and a grilled cheese for Ann. Three cops with bellies hanging over their holsters were sidled up to the register waiting for takeout. I sipped my Coke and kept looking around, waiting for Certain Elements to appear, until Ann figured out what I was doing. "It's his night off, dummy," she said. "I can keep a promise, you know." She pushed her plate away in disgust, and even though I wasn't done with my Coke said, "Let's go."

I paid the cashier—I'd loaded fifteen dollars into my wallet before we left the house—and Ann emptied all the change in her pocket onto the counter for the waitress. We went out into the arcade and kept walking, past a gated-up tobacco store and a florist selling half-dead bouquets. A lot of the stores were closed for the night and the few remaining shoppers looked spent.

I was starting to think I hadn't foxed my sister into anything; whatever Ann really did on Friday nights, this couldn't be it. This was no closer to the real thing than the spookhouses she used to make in the basement, blindfolding me and dipping my hand in bowls of applesauce.

I sighed loudly and Ann said, "Come on, I have to show you something."

I followed her upstairs to the third floor and down the corridor, where I smelled incense. It was coming from a tiny store where a Chinese man in a suit and tie sat behind the counter. He said hello to Ann as if he knew her, then looked at me and said, "I see you brought your sister."

Shelves of merchandise rose all the way to the ceiling: tiny, bright dishes with intricate patterns; birds woven from pink and orange straw; ashtrays with gold Chinese letters; thin, shiny blades that unfolded into fans; teacups; long-tailed kites; necklaces and earrings displayed under glass. My disappointment evaporated.

I picked up a metal turtle and stroked its back. Ann ran her fingers over a red and black plate as if it had a message written in Braille. We picked things up to show each other: tiny sea creatures, cigarette holders, placemats, coasters.

There was nothing in the store I didn't want. I checked the price stickers and finally chose a blue and green vase that curved perfectly in my hand.

"I want this," I told the man, without consulting my sister. I pulled four bills out of my wallet.

"What about me?" Ann said.

"Here." I handed her my wallet. "Take the rest."

Ann sighed. "What I really want—the only thing I really want—is that dragon." She pointed to a huge, jade-colored dragon with red stones for eyes; it was on a high shelf and I hadn't seen it before. "The thing is," she said. "It's thirty dollars."

"In this case," the salesman said, "because you look so much, I'll say twenty-five." Ann looked away and I felt my face go hot. There was about five dollars left in my wallet. Even if I put back the vase and even if we could somehow undo the two Cokes and the grilled cheese, even if we went home and cleaned all the money out of my glass jar, it wouldn't be enough. I felt so bad I would have stolen that dragon, but I couldn't even reach it.

"We'll think about it," Ann said. "Right now we have to go." She headed for the door but I couldn't stand for her to leave emptyhanded. I begged her to pick something else, anything.

"I don't *want* anything else," she said.

Back in the car, I held my vase on my lap. Ann set her pink straw rooster between us on the front seat; she'd picked it out just as the store was closing at nine. Ann lurched into traffic and the rooster tipped over and slid, so she jammed its claws into the crack between the seats. "There," she said, looking at the rooster instead of the road. "I've just decided, this is my lucky bird."

This was the closest I'd get to thanks. She knew I knew she'd never pay me back; also, we were both going to be grounded. I didn't say anything, so Ann punched me on the arm, testing, until I smiled just a little. Then she lit a cig for herself and one for me and turned the volume on the radio up higher. I smoked my fourth and fifth cigs ever on the way home.

"Certain Elements" Discussion

1. At the beginning of the story, what is the relationship between the narrator and her older sister?
2. How does the narrator's perception of her sister change by the end of the story?
3. How are the sisters alike? How are they different?
4. When do you think this story takes place?
5. Do you think Ann is telling the truth when she says it's her boyfriend's night off? If not, why would she lie?
6. What do you think is in store for Ann?
7. What do you think is in store for the narrator?
8. When the narrator observes, "There was nothing in the store I didn't want," she is referring to the myriad of exotic objects

on the Chinese man's shelves. On a grander scale, though, what do you think she is feeling?

Suggestion for Writing

Have you ever felt controlled by an older sibling, or someone else whom you looked up to? Write a description of this person, and include the details that reveal the most about the person. How does he talk? What does she wear? Who are his friends? How does she treat you? How does she treat herself?